DIGITAL
MAGNETIC
RECORDING

DIGITAL
MAGNETIC
RECORDING

ALBERT S. HOAGLAND

IBM Advanced Systems Development Division

JOHN WILEY & SONS, INC.
NEW YORK · LONDON · SYDNEY

PREFACE

Digital magnetic recording is a unique application of magnetic recording technology and has become the technical base of a major new product category, devices for the mass storage of digital data. The advent of the electronic computer with the concomitant growth in information processing has created a tremendous demand for the automated storage and retrieval of masses of data. Digital magnetic recording stands supreme in serving this need and is now an exceedingly important field of applied magnetics. This book represents a pioneer attempt to present a unified treatment of this subject in its own right.

Historically, the initial application of magnetic recording was to the recording and reproduction of sound, where the frequency response characteristic is the particular concern of the designer. In such applications the input-output similitude of a continuous signal waveform is of paramount importance. To draw analogy with circuit theory, the concepts and techniques of analysis appropriate to digital magnetic recording differ from those applicable to such linear recording problems in the same manner and degree as the studies of transient and steady-

v

state network behavior differ from each other. Therefore, with the coming of age of digital magnetic recording, it is felt that a text specialized to this topic will have significant merit.

There are many possible ways to approach the subject of digital magnetic recording, for it involves a range of engineering disciplines and has been built primarily upon practice rather than on theory. After considerable reflection, I came to the following two points of view. First, the essence of this method for recording and reproducing digital data lies in the field of magnetics. Second, in a subject like digital magnetic recording, which has been and still is under intensive development, the most valuable contribution a book can make is to provide a comprehensive understanding and perspective of this storage technology. Therefore, this book stresses digital magnetic recording principles and, through the emphasis on an integrated approach to the subject matter, attempts to illuminate the interrelation and significance of design parameters on the storage of digital information.

The individual merely searching for "cookbook" material will be disappointed. Should he peruse the contents, however, it is felt that he may find his time well spent. Digital magnetic recording is occasionally disparaged as a "black art" precisely because circumstances rarely permit an effective realization of an overall system without close and continuous interaction between the component design activities.

The book should prove useful to the professional working or just beginning in digital magnetic recording, to the student who desires to enhance his understanding in the engineering science of applied magnetics, and to the engineer or scientist investigating the basic problems of data storage. Further, this book should be of value to those in the computer field who are designing or using data-processing systems, for it gives a perspective on the factors setting the status and future potential of digital magnetic recording for mass storage. The book should also serve as an important addition to the fundamental reference sources available to those active in analog magnetic recording.

The introductory chapter gives a descriptive presentation of the phases of the overall magnetic recording operation, along with definitions of common terms. The inherent characteristics of the process of "digital" magnetic recording are presented and elaborated. The influence of mass storage on the design environment for digital magnetic recording is indicated.

The second chapter, Mass Storage, is a completely revised and up-dated version of a paper of this same title written for the Fiftieth Anniversary Issue of the Proceedings of the Institute of Radio Engineers (May 1962). This chapter is a review of the evolution, present status, and future trends in mass data storage. Mass storage devices have been stimulated by, and their rapid evolution has paralleled, the dramatic growth of digital computers and data-processing systems. Since digital magnetic recording is the almost exclusive means for the technological implementation of mass storage, this chapter serves as a valuable background, giving relevance and orientation to the body of the text.

The third chapter reviews the fundamental principles and relations of magnetics relevant to the phenomena in magnetic recording. The principles discussed here form a base for the later theoretical developments. The last section is a presentation of the physical basis of ferromagnetism in terms of magnetic domain behavior.

Chapter 4 covers the theory of the magnetic recording process, specifically from the perspective of digital (or pulse) recording. The input-output relation is characterized in terms of the step function response. The reading and writing operations are each analyzed and then contrasted in terms of their individual impact on performance.

Magnetic heads and magnetic recording media are covered in Chapter 5. Magnetic heads are examined in terms of pulse resolution. Magnetic surfaces are viewed primarily from the viewpoint of their magnetic properties. The phenomenon of self-demagnetization is treated in the context of digital recording, where the recorded pattern is a sequence of discrete magnetization reversals.

Chapter 6 considers the topic of digital magnetic *recording techniques*. This subject represents the "bridge" between recording resolution and bit density. A deliberate attempt has been made to achieve generalizations so that the reader may secure an appreciation of an insight into this facet of digital magnetic recording, rather than merely a compilation of methods that have been used. The latter part of Chapter 6 explores the subject of compensation (or equalization) of the digital magnetic recording channel and the merit of redundancy in the handling of digital data.

Each chapter contains its own list of selected references. The reader who desires an extensive bibliography on magnetic recording is referred to the John Crerar Library, Chicago, Illinois, which has compiled an excellent bibliography on this subject, available in pamphlet form.

This book is an outgrowth of my long participation in the research and development of data storage techniques and devices, based on digital magnetic recording, at the IBM laboratories in San Jose, California. The book only gradually took form, benefitting from lectures given by myself on the subject at the University of California. Indeed, the final draft of the manuscript was prepared in Europe while I was on a special research study concerned with mass data storage. The unstinting support all areas of IBM have given to this task, and especially the initial encouragement of G. L. Tucker, are gratefully acknowledged.

A. S. HOAGLAND

Rotterdam, Netherlands
October, 1963

CONTENTS

1

INTRODUCTION: MAGNETIC RECORDING

Magnetic recording has come into popular, general use for the recording of information only since World War II, but its invention, by the Danish engineer Valdemar Poulson, actually dates back to 1898. A magnetic recording apparatus, which used a steel wire for its storage medium, was publicly demonstrated for the first time at the Paris Exposition in 1900. The recording and reproduction of sound was the initial application of magnetic recording. Despite the promise of the new technique at that time, the recorded signals could be heard only by using earphones. Therefore, interest in magnetic recording gradually lapsed until about 1925, when the emerging possibilities of electronic amplifiers stimulated an increase in activity.

An enormous improvement in the quality of audio magnetic recording was realized in the early 1930's with the combined development of the magnetic oxide surface layer and the ring-type magnetic head, a device suited for recording on a surface. It was not until 1941, however, when the added innovations of superior recording techniques were combined with improved heads and surfaces, that magnetic recording could compete with other sound-recording systems. The development of the art of magnetic recording then began to receive the vastly expanded support that was to assure its rapid growth and acceptance.

The activities that heralded the definitive introduction of the application of magnetic recording to digital data storage were initiated in 1947. This work was instigated in response to the needs of the digital computer field, at this time just entering its explosive growth stage. Digital magnetic recording has acquired and maintained a pre-eminent status as the means for mass data storage. The acceptance and expansion of digital magnetic recording usage parallels the dramatic growth of data processing.

Chapter 2, Mass Storage, provides an illuminating perspective on the significance of digital magnetic recording, where the evolution, status, and future trends in mass storage devices and their technologies are reviewed. The data-processing "revolution" has brought about unceasing demands for larger and larger digital memories which allow relatively rapid access to any unit of data. At the present time, digital magnetic recording represents a major commercial application of magnetics, and all indications point to an increasingly important role for this storage method in the foreseeable future.

Magnetic recording is based on the interaction between a magnetic storage medium and a magnetic head (transducer), in relative motion with respect to one another. The magnetic head magnetizes the magnetic material traversing through a small region immediately adjacent when recording (or writing). The head provides an induced voltage on readback, reflecting the rate of change of magnetization recorded on this magnetic "track."

Magnetic recording depends on the following characteristics of certain ferromagnetic materials. The storage layer must be capable of retaining a sequence of permanent magnetic states, which are directly related to the applied magnetizing field. The recorded pattern is thus stable and can be erased or modified only through re-recording. On the other hand, the transducer (or magnetic head) is a device that has the basic functions of providing a confined and intense magnetizing field at the storage surface (writing) and during reading (or reproduction) a magnetic shunt for surface flux arising from a magnetized state of the recording surface. Both these functions dictate the need for a high-permeability magnetic path with a short non-magnetic section located adjacent to the magnetic surface. Thus, a magnetic head is basically merely a magnetic core possessing a gap and wound with a coil.

Fig. 1.1a illustrates the basic head-surface arrangement in the magnetic recording process and Fig. 1.1b the nature of the recorded magneti-

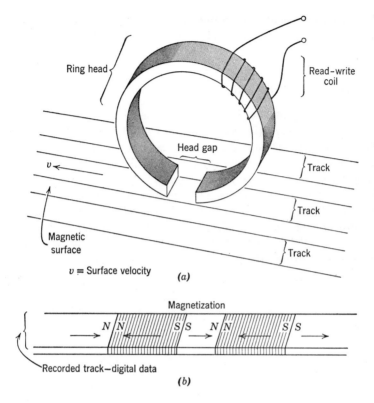

Fig. 1.1. Magnetic recording.

zation. The path generated along the surface by the magnetic head is called a track. A track is thus parallel to the direction of relative motion. The output signal is proportional to the rate of change of flux linking the magnetic head, and hence to the track width. Mechanical considerations have resulted in the relative motion being obtained almost exclusively by moving the surface. Surface area storage is achieved by recording such tracks of information parallel to one another as indicated. Parallel tracks can be recorded by using a complete set of heads (one per track) to provisions for positioning of a single head (or the surface) transverse to the direction of recording or any combination in between. In digital magnetic recording, where the interest is in data storage, a factor frequently of primary importance is the information density per unit area of storage surface. The storage density per unit surface area is the product of the storage density per unit track length times the track density per unit distance normal to the direction of relative motion.

The two components of storage density are interrelated; as noted, an increase in track density will cause a reduction in available readback flux.

MODES OF RECORDING

Three primary modes of recording can be defined, based on the direction of surface magnetization relative to the direction of track motion. These modes are: (1) longitudinal or horizontal recording, (2) perpendicular or vertical recording, and (3) transverse recording.

Fig. 1.2 illustrates these three modes of recording and their associated magnetic head configurations. In longitudinal recording, the principal direction of magnetization is in the plane of the surface and parallel to the direction of surface motion. In vertical recording, the principal orientation of the magnetization is normal to the plane of the surface. In transverse recording, the storage medium is magnetized in the plane of

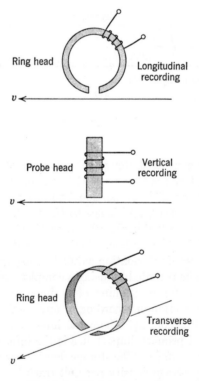

Fig. 1.2. Modes of recording.

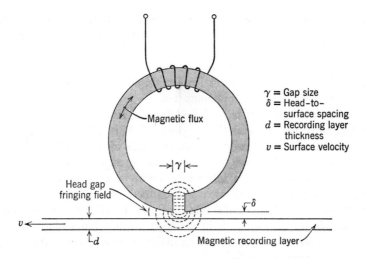

Fig. 1.3. Ring head structure, showing magnetic coupling field.

its surface but normal to the direction of motion between the head and surface.

Longitudinal recording is almost universally used because of the inherent advantages it possesses. A major objective in magnetic recording is to achieve high resolution, that is, a minimum magnetic coupling zone along a track between the head and surface, associated with a satisfactory readback signal-to-noise ratio. A ring head with its gap oriented normal to the direction of relative motion best meets these criteria. Qualitatively it can be seen that a ring head tends to give a more confined field than a probe head, and when oriented for longitudinal recording its width can be adjusted to set the level of read-back flux independent of the resolution. An illustration of the form of magnetic head-to-surface coupling existing with a ring head is given in Fig. 1.3, which shows the gap field with its surrounding leakage flux. The gap fringing field which extends into the magnetic recording surface is the magnetic field of actual utility and interest. Several parameters fundamental to the recording process are also indicated and defined graphically.

DIGITAL MAGNETIC RECORDING

Digital magnetic recording is a unique application of magnetic recording technology. The storage and retrieval of digital data involves the handling of discrete (or quantized) units of information, whereas in other applications of magnetic recording (for example, sound and television recording) the goal is to record and later reproduce as faithful a replica of some continuous input signal waveform as possible. Therefore in digital magnetic recording we are concerned with the writing and reading of pulse-like signals associated with discrete information states. Thus the conceptual framework for our thinking is oriented around discontinuous or transient-like phenomena.

A binary phenomenon is exploited for the recording of digital data. This technique provides for the greatest reliability, for it maximizes the discrimination between recorded surface states with any given operating range and likewise between the corresponding output signals. Further, the magnetization process inherently involves a saturation phenomenon, which gives rise to two well-defined and easily reproducible magnetic states. When digital information is handled by means of only two symbols (or states), it is in a binary form. Each binary digit is commonly referred to as a "bit," and in digital magnetic recording every recorded bit must be individually interpreted—placing a premium on reliable performance. Thus, information is stored in a binary code, customarily utilizing two opposite senses of saturation of the recording medium. These states of saturation can readily be established in terms of the direction of the write current in the write coil. The actual surface magnetization arises from a very complex and non-linear magnetization process, and the surface state can be inferred only by indirect means. For digital recording the writing current has one magnitude and two possible directions, generally corresponding to positive and negative saturation magnetization of the storage medium, determined by the current level at which further increases in current amplitude do not produce an appreciable increase in output voltage on readback.

Fig. 1.4a shows the input current–output voltage relationship in pulse magnetic recording, illustrating the recording saturation characteristic. This property arises from the hysteresis exhibited by the magnetic surface (Fig. 1.4b). This hysteretic behavior is of course responsible for the "storage" feature of magnetic recording.

The inherent differentiation of the recorded magnetization on readback gives a series of alternating voltage pulses, one pulse for each change in direction of surface saturation, for the voltage waveform characterizing digital magnetic recording. This relationship is shown in Fig. 1.5. The readback of binary information involves essentially the ability per bit period to recognize from an attribute of the recovered waveform the bit value (two possibilities only). In digital magnetic recording, signal-detection techniques receive great attention, particularly where high densities are of interest. Chapter 6, Digital Magnetic Recording Techniques, treats this subject in detail.

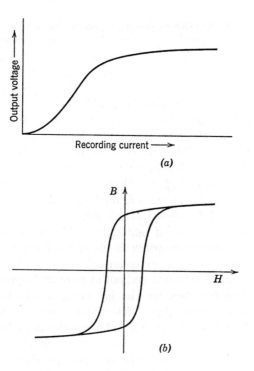

Fig. 1.4. Magnetic saturation phenomena.

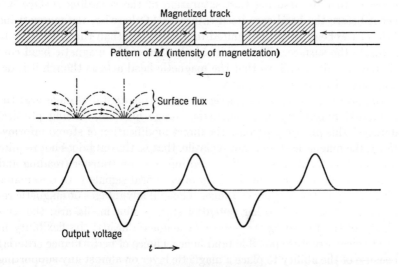

Fig. 1.5. Binary recording.

The magnetic properties appropriate for a storage surface for digital magnetic recording may be qualitatively enumerated more specifically. The value of the maximum-energy product of the surface medium $(BH)_{max}$ should be large. Here, H is the magnetic field intensity and B represents the flux density. The product $(BH)_{max}$ is a measure of the magnetostatic energy which may be stored in a unit volume of material. The induced voltage from the magnetic head on readback is nominally proportional to B_r, the remanence, and hence a large value for this parameter is desirable. Then the coercive force H_c of the medium should be reasonably high to enable the magnetizing operation to proceed with a minimal influence on the region of the track just previously recorded. A relatively large ratio for H_c/B_r will tend to minimize the susceptibility of the surface to self-demagnetizing effects.

The magnetic properties of materials employed for magnetic heads used for digital magnetic recording should be similar in many respects to those sought for high-frequency communication transformers. Since a high speed transfer of data into and out of memory is generally a desired performance objective (set by the bit rate), a high-frequency head characteristic is indicated. Signal detection is dependent on the information detail in the output waveform, and hence the upper frequency range of a magnetic head must be sufficient to give a minimum of waveform distortion. For reading, the initial permeability should be large, this process involving the very weak fields set up by the magnetized surface. For writing, the magnetic head should have a high saturation flux density, thereby assuring that saturation of the recording surface will occur before the head core itself saturates. Otherwise, the magnetizing field of the head would be limited to a value less than that necessary to saturate the surface. The residual induction of the magnetic head core should be quite small, so that the magnetic head acts as though it is de-magnetized when not energized.

Important aspects of magnetic recording for digital storage are: the unlimited reusability of a magnetic storage medium, barring physical damage (this property permits the direct modification of stored information); the magnetic store is non-volatile, that is, the data does not require regeneration for its preservation; and information transfer (reading and writing) occurs directly in the form of electrical signals with obtainable bit rates up in the megacycle range. General advantages of magnetic recording surfaces over other potential storage film media are: the simplicity of the recording transducer (a magnetic head); the flexibility in mechanical structure possible (and hence, choice of performance criteria) because of the ability to place a magnetic layer on almost any supporting surface—in conjunction with ease of mounting a magnetic head; considerable ruggedness with respect to handling and environmental conditions. These features of the magnetic recording process contribute enormously to its attractiveness as a storage means. Associated with these attributes is an extreme economy in terms of cost per bit of storage.

DIGITAL MAGNETIC RECORDING DATA STORAGE

There are two distinct mechanisms utilized for large digital memories. One involves storage on a continuous surface, using a transducer and relative motion for access to data. Digital magnetic recording falls into this class. The other approach to memory involves a matrix-like assembly of individually fabricated bit-storage elements (for example, a coincident current magnetic core array), which are directly addressed and selected by a switching net (see Fig. 1.6). Here, each bit in the plane can be accessed by the concurrent activation of one x and one y select line. Only the core at the selected intersection, defined by its x and y coordinates, will receive the "sum" signal. The latter current is chosen to be above the switching threshold of a core, while the individual selection current components are below this "threshold." This type of data store has a constant access time to any memory location, which is in the range of electronic switching speeds, since no mechanical motion is required.

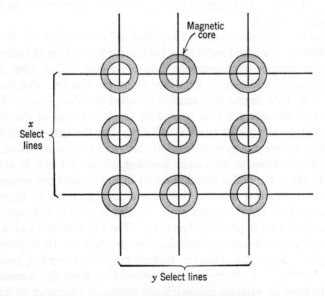

Fig. 1.6. Magnetic core array.

Since each bit is individually "wired," the cost per bit is several orders of magnitude greater than that of digital magnetic recording storage (when very large capacities are considered).

In digital magnetic recording, the bit storage density is principally a function of the registration tolerances that can be realized between the magnetic storage surface(s) and associated magnetic head(s). Although very large capacities (mass storage) can be realized economically, access times to data are in the range of milliseconds to many seconds, since this type of memory involves mechanical movement for data access. Access time to a given storage location is variable, depending on the relative position of the desired surface area to the appropriate magnetic head at the time of a request. The ability to obtain a spectrum of mass storage performance specifications through variations in mechanical structure accounts for the extraordinary innovation in this field of application of magnetic recording.

The present and potential proliferation of mass storage structures makes a presentation of specific devices of questionable value in developing a perspective for digital magnetic recording. Rather than a discussion of hardware, a few generalizations on the nature of structural embodiments of mass storage, reflecting upon the characteristics of the digital magnetic recording process, will be given here. Chapter 2, Mass Storage, reviews in some detail digital magnetic recording from a historical perspective, in terms of its applications environment as well as its technical aspects.

Fig. 1.7 is an illustration of a simplified data-recording unit (rotating disk memory) which will serve as a vehicle for presenting the manner in which performance requirements impact design. The disk sectors shown represent addressable locations along the tracks. The track recorded to provide timing information is called the clock track. The bit rate in data transfer from or to a data track is equal to the product of linear bit density times surface velocity. For the disk device shown, the surface velocity is proportional to the disk rotational speed. The average access time to any data location within a track is equal to $\frac{1}{2}(1/\text{rps})$, where rps is the rotation speed in revolutions per second.

Two aims in mass storage design are to: (a) increase bit-storage capacity, and (b) reduce access time. There is a basic incompatibility between these two objectives, however. The bit resolution of a magnetic head–magnetic surface combination depends on their proximity. Actual physical contact offers the highest potential recording resolution (or bit density). A magnetic field, departing from its source, progressively loses its original geometrically definable character or pattern. Thus, the magnetic field gradient is highest right at the gap and de-

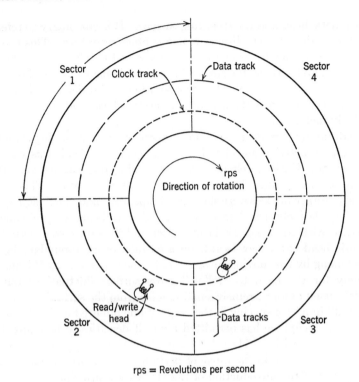

rps = Revolutions per second

Fig. 1.7. Elementary digital recording unit (disk).

creases with distance from the gap, as suggested by Fig. 1.3. This situation differs from electromagnetic wave phenomena where, as in optics, it is possible to focus a light beam at a distance from a source. A progressive deterioration in resolution therefore occurs as the head-to-surface spacing is increased. Magnetic coupling between head and surface as a function of spacing will be treated in detail in Chapter 4. For present purposes this qualitative picture will serve adequately to highlight the influence of the magnetic recording process on mass storage design. The only additional factor to recognize is that in order to keep wear down to an acceptable rate in contact recording, it is necessary to place a limit on surface speed.

Then to maximize capacity we desire to keep the head in intimate contact with the surface. This is inconsistent with minimizing the access time, which, for the single disk unit of Fig. 1.7, is inversely proportional to the surface speed for any given track. Eventually to further reduce access time, it is then necessary to allow for a physical separation between the magnetic head and the recording surface. It is customary to refer to recording under such conditions as non-contact recording. This type of arrangement makes possible a large increase in the relative velocity between head and surface, the surface speed now being established only by mechanical limitations. The loss in resolution (or bit density), however, becomes very severe as the separation between head and surface is progressively increased.

The dramatic "breakthrough" in magnetic recording, arising from the mass storage activity associated with the computer field, was the air-bearing head. Until this element came into being, one had to favor either capacity or access time almost to the exclusion of the other. Therefore the early storage devices were slow-speed tape units and small high-speed drums of relatively low data capacity. This air-bearing development, concerned with the magnetic head carrier and its suspension, permits a magnetic head effectively to ride on a cushion of air (boundary layer) carried along by the moving surface. It has been possible by this means not only for the head to "follow" gross surface fluctuations but to maintain itself at an extremely small spacing from the surface. Here the term small implies a spacing in the range of one hundred millionths of an inch. This technique has permitted high bit densities to be realized at high surface velocities. There has been a broad extension in the types of memory devices and in the range of performance features available as a consequence of the introduction of the air-bearing principle.

Another performance factor of great interest, although not independent of the choice of capacity and access time, is the data-transfer rate. Digital magnetic recording permits of a variety of ways to code and record data in terms of binary digits. Thus, while the bit rate per track is set by bit density and surface speed, data can be stored, on the one hand, in a completely serial manner or, at the other extreme, in a completely parallel manner using many heads operating simultaneously.

Digital magnetic recording is unique as an application for magnetic recording, both in the scope and character of the recording conditions under which it is applied and in the switching or pulse-like nature of the input-output signals. The performance demanded in digital magnetic recording is extreme, for each bit of information is an important entity in its own right and the desired maximum storage densities and minimum access times seemingly have no limiting bound. (There will always be additional data of value to incorporate within an information-processing system if economically feasible). Particular attention is given in later chapters to bit (binary digit) performance limitations imposed by system design parameters.

2

MASS STORAGE

The expanding commercial applications for information-processing systems are increasingly dependent upon the economic availability of on-line memory of extremely large capacity for the automatic servicing of sets of records * (or files). Utility billing and airline reservations systems are two examples of file maintenance requiring "mass storage." The growing need in business operations to have masses of organized information readily available for effective management decision making will accelerate the emergence of computer systems centered around mass storage devices. This trend is likewise reinforced by the pressure for increasingly more sophisticated command and control systems for the military.

In the scientific field of data processing, the temporary storage of intermediate results dictates a mass store which can rapidly interchange data with main memory. In addition, the trend towards computer systems that can perform many jobs concurrently makes a large back-up store for high-speed reloads and dumps of internal memory (program shuffling) advantageous.

* A record is a set of related data on, for example, an individual, a residence, etc.

13

Mass storage is a term used here to imply a unit capacity in excess of one million alphanumeric characters (of the order of 10^7 bits). Certain existing digital magnetic recording mass storage units store more than 100 million characters of data, and technical developments now underway will materially extend this figure.

Such memory capacity is far beyond the present or projected economic feasibility of electronic devices. Solid-state memory is generally based on a matrix-like assembly of individual bit-storage elements (e.g., magnetic core arrays), which are directly addressed and selected by a switching net (12). This type of storage provides high-speed (microsecond) access to any memory location, needed for accomplishing both data and instruction manipulations within a central processor. In contrast, for mass memory continuous storage surfaces (generally interchangeable) with associated coupling transducers are exploited. Relative motion is, of course, required for access to memory locations. Very large capacities are practical, but access times are in milliseconds to many seconds, since mass storage devices involve mechanical movement. The access time variability to memory locations, arising from the requisite mechanical motion, makes the structuring and data organization of mass storage a key factor to effective systems utilization. The recording density (bits per square inch) has proven to be principally a function of the three-dimensional mechanical registration tolerance that can be realized between the storage film (or layer) and the coupling transducer. Typical devices are magnetic tape transports, disk arrays (see Fig. 2.1), drums, etc.

Modularity is an extremely important concept in mass storage. A module is an independently operable block of memory, and a given memory system will in general consist of a number of such modules. Except where the memory is serviced in a true search or scan mode, the storage surface regions are assigned a "machine address," a number which can be translated into appropriate mechanical motions to position the desired data area under a transducer. The most common attributes used to characterize a mass storage module are: capacity; access time (generally defined as the average access time for a large number of randomly located addresses); the instantaneous data rate on serial information transfer; and availability of storage member interchangeability.

The need for operational reliability of mass memory units, devices which involve the integration of complex mechanical and electronic assemblies, has been and still remains one of the major, even though less exciting, challenges to be faced in the further development of mass storage. The trend to communications-oriented data-processing sys-

Fig. 2.1.   IBM RAMAC® disk file.

tems with remote terminals and emphasis on "real-time" response greatly magnifies the importance of performance reliability.

Again, digital magnetic recording is the technology primarily used for the mass storage of digital information. Typical figures place on-line magnetic recording storage at a cost per bit of 1% or less than that for magnetic core memory, the predominant approach for the realization of "electronic stores." The replaceability and off-line shelf storage potential with magnetic recording (for example, tape reels) makes the storage of temporarily inactive data feasible and hence the cost per bit of storage in many cases will be even more orders of magnitude less costly.

Magnetic recording actually embodies the integration of several basic engineering fields and has been generally characterized by rapid progress, achieved by evolutionary advances rather than dramatic innovation. The one "breakthrough" that can be identified with digital magnetic recording in the computer field is the air-floated head. Otherwise, advances in the magnetic recording art have largely emanated from increasingly higher precision and quality in components. No technology that might challenge the position of magnetic recording now appears in sight. Thus, an increasing effort will continue to be placed on magnetic recording and associated mechanisms in spite of their already long period of exploitation.

Certain exploratory work has been carried out on photographic films for the "read only" type of memory applications (for example, language translation and telephone exchange routing). Here, the stored information is of a relatively permanent nature and is compatible with the non-reusable nature of present day photographic media. In such cases, one may capitalize on the ability to carry out high-speed scanning (in a limited region) with an effectively inertia-less optical (i.e., electronic beam) transducer. For a large capacity requiring a great amount of surface area, however, mechanical positioning will be required. The basic access time limitations inherent in any mass store are due to the necessity of some mechanical motion.

The body of this chapter is divided into three major sections: historical evolution of mass storage, present state of the art, and future trends, with emphasis given to key problem areas faced in achieving further progress.

HISTORICAL GROWTH

The work which ushered in mass data storage, as indicated in Chapter 1, was firmly established by 1947. This activity was associated and concurrent with the explosive "take-off" of the digital computer field at that time. Since then, progress has paralleled the rapidly expanding growth of data processing. Early work was oriented to the scientific computer market. The initial mass memory device developed was the digital magnetic tape transport, to provide both auxiliary "back-up" storage to main memory and buffering between the computer and low-speed electromechanical equipment in large-scale systems. In this latter application, tape served as an intermediate medium to permit better matching of the high data-transfer rate of a computer to its low-speed printers, card equipment, etc. The later emergence of commercial data processing brought a wider variety of functional usages and mass storage hardware.

Commercial or business data processing, as it was evolving as a main facet of activity in the computer field in the early 1950's, gave a tremendous impetus to mass storage development and had a major impact on its direction. File storage for records maintenance was the central requirement. The volume of business records certainly justified the introduction of the descriptor "mass."

Magnetic tape was immediately exploited for mass records storage. Tape transports inherently are suited for serial access to information and conventional batch processing procedures (punched card methods) were therefore instituted. The procedure in brief is to sort all requests for file reference into the same order as that in which the basic or master set of records is maintained. Then the master record file tape need be scanned only once (one pass) during the processing run. However, a major percentage of available computer machine time is then needed for the tape sorting of transactions preparatory to processing against a master tape file. For low activity, tape devices are very inefficient. The entire master tape file must be examined no matter how few records are actually referenced. Further, effective file inquiry operations are not possible, the handling of an inquiry involving a momentary interruption of the normal processing to answer an urgent request. To keep head and surface wear down to acceptable rates in contact recording, tape speed is quite limited, representing a restriction on bit rate and access time. Tape speed is also restricted by tape handling problems such as acceleration, deceleration, and maintaining close tolerances on velocity.

The character of much business data processing thus indicated the need for an entirely different type of mass storage. The desirability of storing large volumes of information with any record available rapidly gave stimulus to the development of a mass "random access" memory. The term random access implies that any given address location can be selected more or less directly, without the necessity of scanning through all intervening records located between the present address and the desired address (as must be done for tape). This term will be used henceforth in this somewhat imprecise sense, since it conforms to accepted practice and no more suitable expression has been established. A short (average) access time is then necessary, and a high-speed rotating surface provides this feature. The extremely high surface velocity then arising is only tolerable by providing a slight separation or spacing between the magnetic head(s) and moving surface. This spacing must however be quite small if the concurrent requirement of high capacity is to be realized.

The air-bearing supported head (using an air cushion to control head-to-surface spacing) was the technical innovation which, combined with the above memory concept, brought about this entirely new family of mass storage devices beginning in 1956. By this novel spacing technique, it was possible to develop a high-capacity rotating disk array, for a head could then closely follow the appreciable fluctuation of large disks (a disk stack permits a high figure for magnetic surface area per unit volume).

The first disk file (the IBM RAMAC® 350), see Fig. 2.1, could store five million characters with a maximum access time to any record of less than a second. Note that a single head pair (one head unit for the upper disk faces and one for the lower) is mechanically positioned to service all the tracks within the disk stack. Secondary technical features of significance were the use of self-clocking (deriving bit timing signals from the data itself on readback) and a wide-erase narrow-read/write head unit. This head unit is a special two-element magnetic head structure that erases a path for the selected track just before recording so that precise lateral alignment of the read/write head is not required. These design approaches, combined with the use of an air-supported head, provide techniques that compensate for the head-to-track registration tolerances of such a gross mechanical structure, and thus permit high bit density and high track density, both necessary for a large capacity.

Since the introduction of mass random-access memory, there has been an increasing activity directed to this form of mass storage and a number of units of rather widely varying configurations are now available. One other example, uniquely different in form, is the NCR CRAM (1961), a randomly selectable magnetic card unit. This was the first random-access memory to offer replaceable storage, formerly a feature only available with magnetic tape.

As one perspective on the progress in digital magnetic recording over the last decade, consider storage density.

Univac UNISERVO® I (tape) (1950)	1400 bits per square inch
IBM RAMAC® 350 (disk) (1956)	2000 bits per square inch
Potter 906 (tape) (1960)	24,000 bits per square inch
Univac RANDEX® drum file (1960)	30,000 bits per square inch
IBM 1311 (disk) (1962)	50,000 bits per square inch

These specifications are indicative of both the progress and the emphasis placed on data storage in the last several years. The cost per bit of on-line mass memory has steadily dropped, a major factor responsible for its increasing acceptance. In 1960 it was in the range of 0.1 to 0.01 cents per bit.

PRESENT STATUS

There is such a wide diversity in mechanical configurations for mass storage that attention will be focused primarily on systems perspectives and technology. With respect to magnetic recording, four areas of technical development can be distinguished; magnetic heads, magnetic recording surfaces, head-surface registration mechanics, and read-write electronics. Each of these will be briefly discussed in turn, then the present status of data-storage density, which includes the integrated performance from all these components, will be summarized.

Systems Features

For serial (or sequential) record transfer, the effective character rate is less than the instantaneous rate due to hardware constraints on address location formats. In tape, "inter-record" gaps are used to define record groups for block transfer to main memory and are necessary to accommodate the consequent "start-stop" tape acceleration and deceleration motion. Inter-record gaps to accommodate head switching and mechanical tolerances, although much shorter, are also necessary on high-density disk or drum tracks to make feasible "single-record" selection and modification.

Magnetic tape has been the predominant means for mass storage, and its unique systems features result from the fact that a tape transport (for tape reels) is a completely serial access tape device. The most practical way to use magnetic tape is to identify a record by data forming a part of the record itself (called a key). In updating a file, for example, the master and transaction activity tape reels are read concurrently (all information is arranged and maintained in ordered sequence), and a "new" tape is created on another transport, with the unmodified as well as the altered master records being recorded. Although this procedure is inefficient for low activity files, it is easy to make insertions and deletions as well as to handle variable length records, since physical sections of tape have no specific identity. Further, a tape reel is relatively cheap, and therefore it is practical to store obsoleted data on tape over some time period for security reasons.

Random-access memory involves addressing through physical location to a single record or a particular block of records (one track), which is then scanned. This addressing problem is generally complicated by the fact that the set of "keys" (record identifiers) of a file will, in general, bear no direct relation to the uniform set of machine addresses. For example, a disk memory with one thousand storage locations would have "machine" addresses progressing from 000 to 999. However, if we are storing a set of records on nearly 1000 merchandise items, we have a conversion problem since the item identification would not be derived from such a constrained number set. Various randomizing techniques are used to convert scattered keys, covering an extensive range, to a dense and relatively uniform distribution of numbers to obtain automatic addressing capabilities. Another memory organization technique useful for random-access memory is "chaining," or the linking of arbitrary address locations (records), by recording at a given address location the address of the next desired address location, and so on. Chaining is a systems technique which facilitates setting up automatically record lists on diverse criteria. Random-access memory hardware may also allow "flexible" record length, since intra-track addressing divisions are not basically established by the mechanical structure.

In a random-access memory the record transfer time is generally far less than the access time. Therefore, one data channel can effectively serve a number of access mechanisms, when operating in a true random-access mode of memory accessing. It is often advantageous, then, to build up the total data store from a number of memory modules whose access mechanisms can be overlapped (or concurrently controlled), thereby masking their individual motion times. If the mass storage requirement were visualized as a single functional block, this is a systems approach which may be used to circumvent the technical limitations of mass storage hardware. This modular structure for a mass store places a premium on low-cost design, since it involves a higher ratio of hardware per unit capacity than indicated by the storage volume.

The high data rates with non-contact recording and multiple head groups on a rotating storage unit have made such devices attractive for short-term high-speed main memory dumps and reloads, even though this application requires only sequential data transfer by its very nature.

Magnetic Recording Technology

Magnetic Heads. Magnetic head design skills have advanced to the point where the principal concerns are to evolve fabrication techniques that will provide an improved and smaller precision assembly. Currently, head gaps as small as 20 microinches can be realized. When thin laminations (from $\frac{1}{2}$ to 2 mils) or ferrite pole pieces are used, magnetic heads can yield considerably in excess of 5000 pulses per inch *resolution* with frequency bandwidths extending considerably beyond one megacycle.

Magnetic Recording Surfaces. The mainstream effort in magnetic surface work is the development of higher-quality, thinner recording surfaces rather than a search for improved magnetic properties. There is a broad range for the magnetic properties, within which performance is not noticeably affected.

Magnetic films in use today are (1) oxide coatings formed from a dispersion of either Fe_3O_4 or γ-Fe_2O_3 in an organic binder and (2) Co-Ni platings. Oxide surfaces can be coated to somewhat less than 100 microinches in thickness with a 2-to-5-microinch surface finish. The high quality achieved in oxide magnetic coatings is extraordinary. Disk surfaces are made without any bit defects at 50,000 bits per square inch on a 14-inch diameter disk storing more than 4 million bits. The quality of high-performance magnetic oxide tape is equal or superior to this.

Co-Ni platings require extremely good substrates, since for equivalent linear bit densities it is necessary to go to thinner layers than are required with oxide surfaces. Production run Co-Ni films have been made as thin as 15 microinches, which have proven satisfactory from the viewpoint of quality. The unique advantages of metal films are their superior wear characteristics and their inherent suitability to the production of a very thin magnetic layer, the latter fact giving metallic films an ultimate density potential greater than that projected for the magnetic oxide type layer.

Head-Surface Registration Mechanics. Head-to-surface spacing is the key variable among the design parameters relating to linear bit density in digital magnetic recording. By using the boundary layer of air carried by the moving surface for a bearing, it has been possible to operate reliably at spacings down to 80 microinches while following several thousandths of an inch surface fluctuation. Even in so-called contact recording, an "effective" spacing exists because of surface roughness and contact dynamics.

Read-Write Electronics. Read-write electronics represents a design area where considerable future progress may be unpredictably realized, since it is the aspect affecting density that is least well-defined in terms of theoretical factors to date. From early work based on distinct output pulses and amplitude detection, we now see sophisticated peak-sensing and phase-modulation techniques being exploited, with a consequent capability to operate at higher densities where considerable pulse crowding occurs.

In digital recording, normally *each* bit must be read correctly (although simple parity checking can detect an error and cause a re-read). In this sense, digital magnetic recording is the most demanding application of the magnetic recording art.

Some digital recording standards call for less than one error per billion bits read, and the bit size may be less than one thousandth by twenty thousandth of an inch! Transient variations in head-to-surface spacing (for example, from dust particles) at high densities can cause large signal fluctuations and thereby multiple bit errors. Burst error correction codes (coding the data into binary sequences so that even should several consecutive bits be lost on readback—an error burst—the original message can be reconstructed) and other sophisticated coding techniques now are attracting attention for such high-density digital magnetic recording.

Storage Density. Bit densities in the range of 1000 bits per inch are now common in commercially available digital recording devices. Track densities around 50 tracks per inch are now found in practice. Two criteria establish the limits on this figure: (1) signal-to-noise ratio (head output is proportional to track width); and (2) ability to keep the head and track aligned mechanically. The IBM 1311 disk file stores data at 1000 bpi * and 50 tpi * while the Potter 906 II tape unit records at 1500 bpi and 16 tpi (the much lower ratio of tpi to bpi for tape being typical because of the flexible physical nature of the base medium).

Non-Magnetic Media

A photoscopic disk memory (3) has been developed to serve as a dictionary for language translation. By its very nature, the information can be considered "permanent." The model stores 30 million bits (2000 bpi, 700 tpi) with an access time of about 50 milliseconds. Optical sensing permits "servo tracking" (through an electron beam) with extreme sensitivity, allowing a much closer balance to be obtained between bit and track densities than can be obtained in magnetic recording. A dictionary is an ordered word file particularly organized for rapid reference. A search operation can be executed very efficiently with this photographic device because of the speed of track-to-track repositioning with an electron beam readout mechanism. This application represents an excellent instance in which the advantages of a photographic material for a file are capitalized upon.

Another such example is Minicard (Eastman Kodak). The Minicard system is a document retrieval system in which micro-images (60:1 reduction) are placed on a chip of photographic film along with digital index information.

Thermoplastic tape as a medium for storage is a relatively new innovation. With this material, writing is done by electrically charging the surface, which causes a corresponding surface deformation, and then thermally setting the surface to this information pattern. It has limited reusability, and to date the mechanism must be kept in a vacuum, which limits design flexibility. An electron beam serves as the transducer. Compared to magnetic recording, writing is very slow and reading requires a relatively complex optical system; but its inherent compatibility with electron-optical transducers again leads to a high storage density potential.

* bpi = bits per inch; tpi = tracks per inch.

FUTURE TRENDS

Systems Organization

The trend in data processing systems, extending from applications methodology and procedures to computer organization concepts, will have an impact on the growing role of mass storage. "Real time" will become more meaningful in information processing as there is more and more emphasis on new customer services and on management decision making. The evolution of lower-cost random-access mass storage will greatly influence the growth of information storage and retrieval systems, an application area that is quite cost sensitive.

The trend in the future will be to optimize memory structure around the random plus sequential capabilities inherently present in a mass storage device. Consider a typical random-access disk memory which has an average access time of 100 milliseconds and a character rate of 50 kc (fifty thousand characters per second) and which contains a file consisting of records of 100 characters each. The effective record transfer rate with sequential scanning is nearly 500 per second, whereas for purely random access transfers this figure would drop to 10. This wide differential highlights the desirability of a random-sequential data-processing philosophy for mass storage exploitation.

With a random-access memory, one frequently uses the terms "response time" and "throughput." Response time is the average time delay between the request for specific data and its receipt. The minimum figure for the response time is the (average) access time, implying that no previous access request is still waiting to be served or currently being serviced. The term throughput is usually used to describe the average number of independent data transfers (to or from the mass storage) per second. Obviously, this figure can vary widely, depending on the queuing discipline in the address request list. Special logic control facilities will be introduced for ordering memory request queues to balance throughput versus response time as a function of the computer program.

A major problem in large data-processing complexes is to establish the proper balance of mass storage configurations. A hierarchy of memory modules (of widely varied performances), integrated to meet total systems requirements, will generally best optimize overall systems performance, recognizing that cost tends to be inversely related to access time for a given capacity. Control logic will eventually extend to the functional ability to rearrange records readily according to their activity, within the hierarchy of memory, significantly improving the utilization of access hardware. The concept of several processors working against a common mass storage will become established, radically changing the perspective of what is the "attachment" and what is the "mainframe."

For the immediate future, off-line storage must be used where possible for economy, but in time it should be possible to maintain larger quantities of storage on-line and transfer increasingly inactive information successively to cheaper (and consequently longer-access) sections of memory until it truly becomes archival. In time, cost reductions will also make it possible to leave a relatively high percent of available memory space unassigned. This fact will greatly simplify the organization of data within memory.

Mass Storage Structure

There will be continuous efforts at cost reduction to make larger capacities for mass storage more economic. The cost of on-line mass storage is a major barrier today to numerous applications susceptible to data processing, some proposed systems requiring the on-line storage of billions of characters with response times in the order of a second to permit an effective man-machine interface. Production manufacturing techniques are rapidly improving, also indicating that smaller mass storage devices will soon impact the conventional electromechanical accounting equipment area. The storage of interlaced (or multiplexed) data and/or the balancing of mechanical motions between surface and transducer movement may be introduced as a technique to set character rate independently while permitting the upgrading of capacity and access speed as technology progresses.

Looking to the future, there appear to be two unique mechanical approaches that will eventually characterize the principal on-line mass storage systems component. One is the disk array and the other is the magnetic strip file. The former offers both a more economic access modularity, although this advantage is achieved through acceptance of a common disk drive (single shaft), and a low-cost "turntable" potential for smaller capacity replaceable disk pack storage. The tape-strip memory uses basically a tape-strip cartridge with random access strip selection, emphasizing simplicity of interchangeability as well as high volumetric efficiency for extremely large capacity.

Reliability Considerations

A major problem, which must be approached from a systems (as well as a technical) viewpoint, is that of high reliability. Achieving extreme reliability represents a challenging task in complex electromechanical assemblies, which are at the same time intimately integrated with high-speed, low-signal-level electronics. Increasing performance demands coupled with growing requirements for on-line "real-time" information availability compounds this problem.

In many random-access memories, it is currently standard practice to automatically provide an address compare by recording the actual address of the physical location in the first section of the record stored there, which can then be checked with the address register. It is also highly advantageous to make a readback check after writing to provide confirmation of proper data recording before the source information is eradicated. While some tape transports provide immediate readback checking by means of a special dual-element head unit, a separate read cycle has been required after writing to fulfill this function in mass storage devices that use head positioning. Special head structures to provide this checking feature automatically, without an access time penalty, will evolve for most forms of mass storage. This capability will also bring about automatic data re-allocation without system interruption when defective storage surface regions are detected.

Systems organization must provide for the requirements of operational reliability by suitably accommodating occasional hardware failures and maintenance needs. Replaceable storage concepts will be increasingly exploited, since the storage member can then be placed on another mechanism to continue file processing during "down time."

Technology

Continuing investigations made of a magnetic recording unit regarded as a communications channel will yield further bit-density gains by the acceptance of more sophisticated recording electronics. To date, advances in bit density have been based primarily on scaling down the magnetic recording "geometry"; however, with no new storage technology warranting a redirection of activity, signal-handling techniques will eventually draw major attention.

There has been and will be continuing exploratory research on novel transducers. However, no physical phenomena for a magnetic recording transducer appear to compete with the simplicity and flexibility of a magnetic head. Rather, the next major stage of progress in the transducer area will likely be automated head fabrication using thin film technology (rather than watchmaker-like assembly), resulting in cost reductions which will eventually have an impact on the hardware composition of mass storage mechanisms.

Reduced head-to-surface spacings, approaching the theoretical limits for air-bearing heads in a normal atmosphere of about 25 microinches, will bring about a large increase in non-contact recording bit density. Track seeking and "following" servo-access techniques, which can circumvent the track density limitations imposed by the buildup of cascaded mechanical dimension tolerances, will be applied to effect significant increases in this parameter (15). Within the next few years one million bits per square inch (e.g., approximately 5000 bpi, 200 tpi) will become the "state of the art" in digital magnetic recording.

There is continuing work looking to the development of other and hopefully better film media for mass storage. There appears no evidence to suggest that a replacement can be soon anticipated for magnetic recording surfaces. Further, the upper magnetic bit-density limit of magnetic surfaces is far in excess of present practice and laboratory studies. For the foreseeable future it is clear that mass storage, based on magnetic recording, has a vital and increasingly important future in information processing.

REFERENCES *

1. "IBM magnetic tape reader and recorder," W. S. Buslik, *Proceedings of the Eastern Joint Computer Conference*, New York, December 10–12, 1952, pp. 86–90.
2. "Notched-Disk Memory," J. Rabinow, *Electrical Engineering*, Vol. 71, August 1952, pp. 745–749.
3. "Photographic techniques for information storage," G. W. King, G. W. Brown, and L. N. Ridenour, *Proceedings of the IRE*, Vol. 41, October 1953, pp. 1421–1428.
4. "Air floating, a new principle in magnetic recording of information," G. E. Hanen, *Computers and Automation*, Vol. 2, November 1953, pp. 23–25.
5. "Engineering design of a magnetic-disk random-access memory," T. Noyes and W. E. Dickinson, *Proceedings of the Western Joint Computer Conference*, San Francisco, February 7–9, 1956, pp. 42–44.
6. "Datafile—A new tool for extensive file storage," D. N. MacDonald, *Proceedings of the Eastern Joint Computer Conference*, New York, December 10–12, 1956, pp. 124–127.
7. "The random-access memory accounting machine, system organization," M. L. Lesser and J. W. Haanstra, *IBM Journal of Research and Development*, Vol. 1, January 1957, pp. 62–71.
8. "Addressing for random-access storage," W. W. Peterson, *IBM Journal of Research and Development*, Vol. 1, April 1957, pp. 130–146.
9. "Role of large memories in scientific communications," M. M. Astrahan, *IBM Journal of Research and Development*, Vol. 2, October 1958, pp. 310–313.
10. "Programming Business Computers," D. D. McCracken, *et al.*, John Wiley and Sons, New York, 1959.
11. "Thermoplastic recording," W. E. Glenn, *Journal of Applied Physics*, Vol. 30, December 1959, pp. 1870–1873.

* Pioneer work or generalized treatments.

12. "Computer memories: A survey of the state-of-the-art," J. A. Rajchman, *Proceedings of the IRE*, Vol. 49, January 1961, pp. 104–127.

13. "High density digital magnetic recording techniques," A. S. Hoagland and G. C. Bacon, *Proceedings of the IRE*, Vol. 49, January 1961, pp. 258–268.

14. *Proceedings of the Symposium on Large Capacity Memory Techniques for Computing Systems*, Information Systems Branch, Office of Naval Research, Washington, D. C., May 23–25, 1961.

15. "A high track density servo access system for magnetic recording disk storage," A. S. Hoagland, *IBM Journal of Research and Development*, Vol. 5, October 1961, pp. 287–296.

16. "Mass Storage," A. S. Hoagland, *Proceedings of the IRE*, Vol. 50, May 1962, pp. 1087–1092.

3

PRINCIPLES OF MAGNETICS

This chapter presents a review of the principles of magnetics, oriented to the fundamentals relevant to a satisfactory understanding of the digital magnetic recording process. Primary emphasis is given to concepts and mathematical tools useful in dealing with macroscopic magnetic phenomena. A brief treatment of the physical basis for ferromagnetic behavior is included, serving to relate the internal structure of magnetic materials to their external properties.

While magnetic phenomena are generally highly non-linear, many problems are tractable to conventional mathematical formulation, where piece-wise linearity is assumed. The principles presented in this chapter have been extremely valuable, in both a qualitative and a quantitative sense, in yielding a theoretical base for digital magnetic recording. This success is due both to careful analysis of the nature of of the problem and to recognition of various ranges within which a valid mathematical model can be constructed. It is as important to be aware of the inherent limitations of the concepts and mathematical relations developed, as of their fundamental meaning and significance.

This chapter attempts to or-

28

ganize and present a set of concepts and relations providing a coherent treatment of the subject, rather than to cover only those aspects explicitly introduced in the subsequent chapters. Magnetic fields involve vector quantities, and some familiarity with vector notation and identities is assumed in the material to follow. A set of references is given at the end of this chapter, to assist the reader who wishes to pursue the subject matter further.

HISTORICAL BACKGROUND

Before Oersted's discovery in 1820 that an electric current would affect a magnetic needle, magnetism as a branch of physical science was completely independent of the theory of electricity. Following this discovery, Ampère quickly investigated, both experimentally and mathematically, the mutual forces between currents and showed (1825) that a current in a circuit is equivalent to a "magnetic shell" of calculable strength. He considered that a "magnet" gives rise to an external magnetic field produced by circulating electrical currents within the molecules of the material. This concept, though not immediately accepted because there was no way to prove or disprove it, stood the test of time and was elaborated upon only by the advent of electron theory.

We shall find it most advantageous to approach the subject of magnetics in terms of its association with current flow. Ampère's law gives the relation governing the force that one current carrying conductor will exert on another and serves as the basis for the definition of a magnetic field. A current element is a vector, that is, it possesses both magnitude and direction, and therefore the force equation involves vector quantities. The mks system is used except for quantitative values of field quantities where the emu system of units is standard (Oersted and Gauss for magnetic field intensity and flux density respectively). Boldface type is used to distinguish a vector quantity from a scalar quantity.

The force on a differential length of conductor, $d\mathbf{l}_1$, carrying a current i, is

$$d\mathbf{F} = i_1 \, d\mathbf{l}_1 \times \mathbf{B} \tag{3.1}$$

where $\mathbf{B}$ is defined in terms of this force and is called the magnetic flux density or magnetic induction. $\mathbf{B}$ is a field then related to the current in the second length of conductor by the following equation:

$$d\mathbf{B} = \frac{\mu_0}{4\pi} \frac{i_2 \, d\mathbf{l}_2 \times \mathbf{r}}{r^3} \tag{3.2}$$

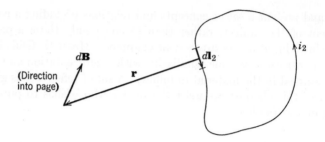

Fig. 3.1. Incremental field arising from a current element.

The vector distance from the current element $i_2 \, dl_2$ to the point at which $d\mathbf{B}$ is to be determined is **r**. μ_0 is a constant defined as the permeability of free space. The vectors from both these equations are the result of a vector or cross-product operation, symbolized by **×**, and accordingly are perpendicular to the plane described by the component vectors of the product (see Fig. 3.1). The total field arising from a complete current loop is obtained by integration, summing up the contributions from the differential current elements.

For example, equation (3.2) may be readily applied to calculate the field produced at the center of a circular current loop. In this instance, r is equal to a, the radius of the loop; dl and **r** are mutually perpendicular, so that their cross product is merely $a \, dl$ and all the differential contributions, $d\mathbf{B}$, are parallel (and hence directly additive).

Since for a sector, $d\theta$, of a circle $dl = a \, d\theta$ (where θ is in radians)

$$d\mathbf{B} = \frac{\mu_0 i}{4\pi} \frac{(a \, d\theta)}{a^2} \mathbf{a}_n$$

where $\mathbf{a}_n$ is a unit vector perpendicular to the plane of the current loop and

$$\mathbf{B} = \mathbf{a}_n \frac{\mu_0 i}{4\pi a} \int_0^{2\pi} d\theta = \frac{\mu_0 i}{2a} \mathbf{a}_n \tag{3.3}$$

The above phenomena are concerned with static or quasi-static currents. In 1829 Joseph Henry, while experimenting with an electromagnet, noticed the spark that occurred when the circuit was broken, and he was led to the discovery of self-induction. The same phenomenon was independently discovered by Michael Faraday, who was the first to publish results. These discoveries led to the formulation of the law governing the relation between induced voltage and the rate of change of flux linkages, usually known as Faraday's law of induction. This relation can normally be written as follows:

$$e = \frac{N\,d\phi}{dt} = \frac{d\Phi}{dt} \tag{3.4}$$

where ϕ is the total flux linking the circuit. The flux can be directly determined from the flux density, **B**. N is equal to the number of turns composing the loop or coil.

The experimentally derived laws of electricity and magnetism were formulated and combined systematically in mathematical equations by James Clerk Maxwell, whose famous treatise was published in 1873.

MAGNETIC FIELD RELATIONS *

We can accommodate magnetic materials in the extensions of the theory given by considering them to give rise to magnetic fields through microscopic "magnetization" currents within their internal structure. This latter concept is consistent with the absence of free magnetic charge in nature. However, since we cannot actually measure such currents, it is necessary to define magnetic properties in terms of the resulting magnetic field arising from the presence of magnetic media.

Current flow is continuous, or more generally, the current density is everywhere solenoidal. Then from the form of the expression for **B** in equation (3.2) we can write

$$\nabla \cdot \mathbf{B} = 0 \tag{3.5}$$

This equation expresses a differential relation for the field vector **B**. The symbol $\nabla \cdot$ denotes "the divergence of." The symbol ∇ is the gradient operator, and the dot indicates a scalar or dot product. This equation is another way of stating that the flux density is everywhere continuous, there being no sources or sinks for **B**.

Gauss's theorem (for generalized vector fields) gives

$$\int_v \nabla \cdot \mathbf{B}\, dv = \oint_s \mathbf{B} \cdot d\mathbf{s} \tag{3.6}$$

Here, v indicates a volume, and s indicates the enclosing surface. Considering the divergence of any vector as a density of outward flux flow from a point for that vector, the total flux emanating from a closed region must be obtained by integrating the divergence throughout the volume.

---

* Static or quasi-static fields (valid for the description of magnetic recording phenomena).

Thus

$$\oint_s \mathbf{B} \cdot d\mathbf{s} = 0 \tag{3.7}$$

This integral can be interpreted as expressing the fact that the net magnetic flux flowing through a closed surface is zero.

In addition, since $\mathbf{B}$ is to be defined only in terms of current sources, based on equation (3.2),

$$\nabla \times \mathbf{B} = \mu_0 \mathbf{j} \tag{3.8}$$

where $\nabla \times \mathbf{B}$ is the curl of $\mathbf{B}$, and $\mathbf{j}$ is the current density at a given point. The integral form of this relation is

$$\oint \mathbf{B} \cdot d\mathbf{l} = \mu_0 I \tag{3.9}$$

or, the line integral of $\mathbf{B}$ around any closed path is equal to μ_0 times the *net* current enclosed.

This latter expression, for example, permits ready calculation of the field at a distance $\mathbf{r}$ from an infinitely long straight wire carrying a current I. Selecting a circular path, distant r from the wire we have (symmetry indicating that $\mathbf{B}$ is only a function of r)

$$\oint \mathbf{B} \cdot d\mathbf{l} = \int_0^{2\pi} B(r)\, r\, d\theta = B \cdot 2\pi r = \mu_0 I$$

or

$$B = \frac{\mu_0 I}{2\pi r} \tag{3.10}$$

In a magnetic medium the current density $\mathbf{j}$ may arise from two contributing sources, that is,

$$\nabla \times \mathbf{B} = \mu_0(\mathbf{j}_t + \mathbf{j}_m) \tag{3.11}$$

where $\mathbf{j}_t$ is a measurable (or true) conduction current density and $\mathbf{j}_m$ is a so-called magnetization current density accounting for the presence of the magnetic medium. We can set

$$\mathbf{j}_m = \nabla \times \mathbf{M} \tag{3.12}$$

where $\mathbf{M}$ is defined as the magnetic moment per unit volume or intensity of magnetization of the material. It should be recalled that the basic experimental quantity measured in determining the presence of magnetism in a body is torque (which is a function of the magnetic moment), since isolated magnetic poles do not exist. Rewriting equation (3.11) we have

$$\nabla \times (\mathbf{B} - \mu_0\mathbf{M}) = \mu_0\mathbf{j}_t \tag{3.13}$$

Let us now define a new magnetic field vector **H** as follows:

$$\mathbf{H} = \frac{1}{\mu_0} [\mathbf{B} - \mu_0\mathbf{M}] \tag{3.14}$$

then

$$\nabla \times \mathbf{H} = \mathbf{j}_t \tag{3.15}$$

We have by this means defined a magnetic field quantity (H = magnetic field intensity) whose curl or circulation density is dependent only on the actual currents in the system. The integral form of equation (3.15) is

$$\oint \mathbf{H} \cdot d\mathbf{l} = I \tag{3.16}$$

By the approach taken here, it is seen that **B** is the fundamental magnetic field vector and **H** is a derived quantity. This procedure is more in accord with the true nature of magnetic field sources, although one can also start with **H** as the basic magnetic field quantity. The latter perspective results if magnetic fields are postulated starting from the premise of the existence of free magnetic poles, drawing a correspondence with the electrostatic field. It will be found mathematically convenient to use both of these magnetic field vectors as basic concepts with which to deal with the diverse problems encountered in applied magnetics. Again, they are distinguished by the fact that the circulation density of the **H** field arises from true currents, and that of the **B** field arises from true currents plus "magnetization currents." Since the postulated "magnetization currents" exist only within magnetic media (to account for its magnetic behavior), the vectors **B** and **H** only differ essentially within magnetic regions.

If we take the divergence of both sides of equation (3.14) we have

$$\nabla \cdot \mathbf{H} = -\nabla \cdot \mathbf{M} \tag{3.17}$$

since, as already shown,

$$\nabla \cdot \mathbf{B} = 0$$

Thus the magnetic field intensity vector **H** can be thought of as arising from a magnetic charge source density ρ_m where

$$\rho_m = -\nabla \cdot \mathbf{M} \tag{3.18}$$

One unit of this equivalent magnetic charge density is usually known as a magnetic pole. In terms of this definition a magnetic pole has no physical justification, other than that the mathematical description of the field **H** is then formally the same as that for the electrical field due to electric charges.

In the absence of current sources

$$\nabla \times \mathbf{H} = 0 \qquad (3.19)$$

This condition implies that the magnetic field intensity can be derived from a scalar magnetic potential function.

Thus, we can set

$$\mathbf{H} = -\nabla \phi_m \qquad (3.20)$$

where ϕ_m is a scalar. This latter fact is extremely important, since it is far easier to deal with scalar quantities. When **H** is expressed as the gradient of a scalar,

$$\int_a^b \mathbf{H} \cdot d\mathbf{l} = \int_a^b d\phi_m = \phi_m(b) - \phi_m(a)$$

Thus a line integral is only a function of the potential difference between its end points and independent of the path. For a closed path

$$\oint \mathbf{H} \cdot d\mathbf{l} = 0$$

To illustrate the relation between the magnetic field vectors we shall consider qualitatively the fields associated with a circular cylinder homogeneously magnetized in the direction of its axis. We will assume **M** to be independent of external fields. From equation (3.13)

$$\nabla \times \mathbf{B} = \mu_0 \nabla \times \mathbf{M} \qquad (3.21)$$

The curl of **M** is zero except on the curved surface of the cylinder where the magnetization **M** changes discontinuously from **M** to 0. All internal magnetization currents cancel, and the hypothetical surface currents are the only effective magnetization current sources. Further, the divergence of **M** is equal to zero except on the two end faces, where on one end there is a surface divergence of amount $+M$ and on the other end $-M$.

B, the magnetic flux density, can then be viewed as arising from an equivalent solenoid, which can be thought of as being wound on the

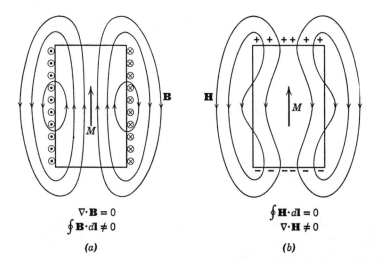

$$\nabla \cdot \mathbf{B} = 0$$
$$\oint \mathbf{B} \cdot d\mathbf{l} \neq 0$$

$$(a)$$

$$\oint \mathbf{H} \cdot d\mathbf{l} = 0$$
$$\nabla \cdot \mathbf{H} \neq 0$$

$$(b)$$

Fig. 3.2. B and H fields of a permanent magnet.

cylindrical surface of the magnet. The lines of force thus resulting are shown in Fig. 3.2a. On the other hand, H can be considered as arising from a layer of magnetic pole charges located on the faces of the magnet, as illustrated in Fig. 3.2b. These two pictures represent equivalent means of representing the same facts, and depending on the objective one may be preferable to the other. Below each figure are given the basic vector relations establishing the nature of each field. We know from equation (3.14) that $\mathbf{B}/\mu_0$ and H are identical outside of the region where M exists, but they differ by M inside the magnet. In fact, B and H are actually opposite in direction within the magnet, which is obvious from the fact that the line integral of H must be zero about any closed path. It is seen that the H field *inside* the magnet opposes M (its own source) and for this reason is referred to as a demagnetizing field.

Magnetic Permeability

Thus far we have considered the case where the intensity of magnetization M is a given function of position, as in an ideal permanent magnet. Let us next examine the situation in which we have an ideally permeable medium, that is, a medium which has no magnetic moment in the absence of external currents and which gives rise to a magnetic moment per unit volume proportional to the field produced by the external currents. The field equations that will consistently apply are:

$$\nabla \cdot \mathbf{B} = 0$$

$$\oint \mathbf{H} \cdot d\mathbf{l} = I$$

For such a linear medium as postulated, we can set

$$\mathbf{M} = \chi_m \mathbf{H} \tag{3.22}$$

where χ_m is called the magnetic susceptibility. Then, setting $\mu = \chi_m + 1$ and using equation (3.14), we have

$$\mathbf{B} = \mu \mu_0 \mathbf{H} \tag{3.23}$$

where μ is the relative permeability of the magnetic material.

For such linear media the boundary conditions for B and H may be shown to be (in the absence of surface currents)

$$B_2 = B_1; \; \mu_2 H_2 = \mu_1 H_1 \text{ (normal components)}$$

$$H_2 = H_1; \; B_2/\mu_2 = B_1/\mu_1 \text{ (tangential components)}$$

In general M and H have a very complex non-linear relationship, and therefore this simple concept of permeability will have meaning only over specified narrow operating ranges.

Equivalence, Magnetic Shell–Current Loop

A useful relation in formulating many problems in magnetics is the equivalence between a current loop and a magnetic shell. A magnetic shell is a surface possessing a uniform magnetic dipole distribution. The dipole density is simply the magnetic moment per unit area. This equivalence in actuality amounts to no more than a restatement of the fact that a magnetized region is equivalent to a current distribution of density

$$\mathbf{j}_m = \nabla \times \mathbf{M}$$

and supports Ampère's interpretation of magnetism in terms of infinitesimal circulating currents.

It can be shown (2) that the magnetic moment of an infinitesimal current loop is equal to

$$d\mathbf{m} = I \, d\mathbf{a} \tag{3.24}$$

where $d\mathbf{m}$ is the magnetic moment, I the current, and $d\mathbf{a}$ the infinitesimal plane area. The vector $d\mathbf{a}$ (and hence $d\mathbf{m}$) is normal to this plane. The elementary moment depends on the current and area enclosed by the

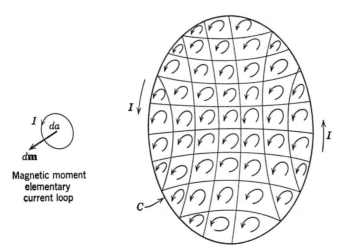

Fig. 3.3. Resolution of current loop C into a network of elementary current loops.

circuit, not on its particular form. (Note that $d\mathbf{m} = \mathbf{M}\,dv$ for a differential volume of magnetic material).

Any circuit contour can be resolved into a system of elementary currents. Consider a network of intersecting lines on some surface spanning the current contour C (see Fig. 3.3). Imagine that about the contour of each elementary area there is a current I equal in magnitude to the current in C. The magnetic field produced by this network of currents is everywhere identical with that of the current I in the simple contour C; for all the interior currents cancel one another. Clearly in the limit, as the fineness of division increases, the field is identical with that of a dipole distribution over the spanning surface. The dipole density, or moment per unit area, of the equivalent surface distribution is constant and equal to

$$\tau = \frac{dm}{da} = I \tag{3.25}$$

Another perspective from which to draw this analogy is through consideration of the scalar magnetic potential of a magnetic shell and a current loop. (A scalar magnetic potential cannot be used if line integrals are considered which encircle current-carrying regions.)

For a magnetic shell it can be shown (2) that

$$\phi_m(x, y, z) = \frac{\tau}{4\pi}\,\Omega \tag{3.26}$$

where again τ is the dipole density and Ω is the solid angle subtended by the shell at the point (x, y, z). For a current loop

$$\phi_m(x, y, z) = \frac{I}{4\pi} \Omega \tag{3.27}$$

where I is the current in the loop and Ω is established by the loop contour.

Since

$$d\phi_m = \frac{\tau}{4\pi} d\Omega \tag{3.28}$$

the discontinuity in the magnetic scalar potential ϕ_m across the selected dipole surface spanning the loop is

$$\phi_{m^+} - \phi_{m^-} = \tau \tag{3.29}$$

corresponding to the change in solid angle of 4π. This result from the magnetic shell analogy correlates with the previously derived relation for the line integral of the magnetic field $\mathbf{H}$.

Recall that

$$\oint \mathbf{H} \cdot d\mathbf{l} = I$$

about any closed path linking the current loop and this result must also obtain from the equivalent magnetic shell.

Note carefully that the equivalent magnetic shell could be any arbitrary surface spanning the current contour. Therefore, it serves as a mathematical convenience rather than a representation of a physical identity.

MAGNETIC FIELD BOUNDARY VALUE PROBLEMS

Magnetic recording behavior depends very significantly on the distribution of magnetic fields in space. In all but a very few idealized instances, the only applicable techniques for predicting the spatial distribution of a magnetic field are graphical mapping, analog methods of field plotting, and numerical calculation using difference equations. This section will briefly sketch the bases of these approaches. The extremely small physical dimensions of the typical region of concern in magnetic recording preclude suitable and convenient instrumentation. Therefore, it is necessary to place great emphasis and reliance on these modeling techniques. Depending on circumstances, each may have particular advantages.

Since our interest in magnetic field configurations is concerned primarily with current free regions, where

$$\nabla \times \mathbf{H} = 0 \qquad (3.30)$$

we can then write $\mathbf{H}$ as the gradient of a scalar, that is,

$$\mathbf{H} = -\nabla \phi_m$$

In all regions where

$$\nabla \cdot \mathbf{H} = -\nabla \cdot \mathbf{M} = 0$$

then

$$\nabla^2 \phi_m = 0 \qquad (3.31)$$

The latter equation is known as Laplace's equation. The divergence of $\mathbf{M}$ will be zero in all media where the permeability is constant. Therefore we can obtain the magnetic field in free space through solution of Laplace's equation and in those magnetic media where it is valid to approximate the ratio of $\mathbf{B}$ to $\mathbf{H}$ by a constant.

The boundary conditions on $\mathbf{H}$ and $\mathbf{B}$ between two magnetic regions of different constant permeabilities have already been stated. These boundary conditions provide the means to match the magnetic field across the interface between two magnetic media. For a magnetic region of sufficiently high permeability, μ can be assumed infinite and a magnetic field emerging into free space will be normal to the bounding surface. In this case, the surface boundary will be an equipotential line of the scalar magnetic potential function.

All points of a magnetic field having the same potential may be thought of as connected by an equipotential surface. The magnetic field vector must be perpendicular to these surfaces at every point, since we have seen that

$$\int_a^b \mathbf{H}\, d\mathbf{l} = \phi_m\,(b) - \phi_m\,(a) \qquad (3.32)$$

and along an equipotential by definition $\phi_m\,(b) = \phi_m\,(a)$ irrespective of the separation between point b and point a. It is particularly convenient to work directly with magnetic potentials, not only because they are scalar functions but because, in general, the boundary conditions will be identified in terms of a potential. In particular for regions where the relative permeability can be considered infinite (the permeability of air being 1), the boundary surface directly defines a potential line.

For a two-dimensional field a graph of equipotential and field lines must divide the plane into curvilinear rectangles, where the field and potential lines are orthogonal. The usual procedure is to divide the space between known potential lines (boundaries) into a certain number

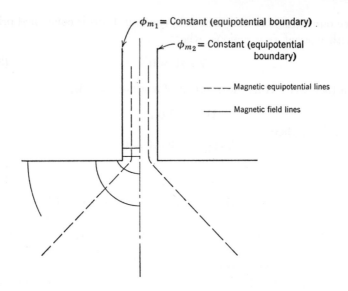

Fig. 3.4. Graphical development of a magnetic field configuration.

of equal intervals through subdividing equipotential lines. Then field lines are generally inserted in attempt to establish a net of curvilinear squares, although the requirement of meeting orthogonality is placed first. See Fig. 3.4 for such an attempt. Successive revisions using this procedure will lead to an improved field plot (6).

Analog methods of determining magnetic fields are based on the fact that in a conducting medium of constant resistivity the voltage distribution must satisfy Laplace's equation. Further, electrical conductors, since they do not support a significant potential gradient in comparison with resistive media (electrolytes, etc.), provide an excellent means to represent equipotential boundaries. Therefore, it is relatively easy to make an electrical analog of many magnetic structures. The advantage of this approach is the ease of plotting potential lines with a voltage probe as well as the simplicity of forming scale models of greatly increased size to facilitate instrumentation.

Once the potential plot is made, the force field can be determined from

$$\mathbf{H} = -\nabla \phi_m$$

or

$$H_x = \frac{-\partial \phi_m}{\partial x} \tag{3.33a}$$

and

$$H_y = \frac{-\partial \phi_m}{\partial y} \tag{3.33b}$$

for a two-dimensional field under investigation. Fortunately, in magnetic recording a two-dimensional model of the magnetic structure is generally valid.

Laplace's equation can also be solved by numerical methods. Electronic computers now make this technique very feasible. A net of points is established, and after the boundary conditions are fixed an iterative process is used to adjust the inner potentials until an acceptable level of stability or equilibrium is reached.

For a two-dimensional case

$$\nabla^2 \phi_m = \frac{\partial^2 \phi_m}{\partial x^2} + \frac{\partial^2 \phi_m}{\partial y^2} \tag{3.34}$$

Using finite differences, consider the mesh point in Fig. 3.5. Let $\Delta x = \Delta y = 1$. Then

$$\nabla^2 \phi_m = [\phi_m\,(a) - \phi_m\,(P)] - [\phi_m\,(P) - \phi_m\,(c)]$$

$$+ [\phi_m\,(d) - \phi_m\,(P)] - [\phi_m\,(P) - \phi_m\,(b)] = 0 \tag{3.35}$$

or

$$\phi_m\,(P) = \frac{[\phi_m\,(a) + \phi_m\,(b) + \phi_m\,(c) + \phi_m\,(d)]}{4} \tag{3.36}$$

The latter equation states that the potential of any point is equal to the average value of the potentials on its "boundary." Successive iterations over such a mesh is a convergent process. The fineness of the net

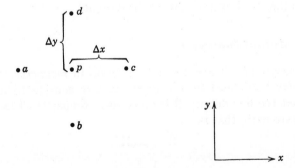

Fig. 3.5. Mesh point and surrounding neighbors.

of points chosen must be commensurate with the actual accuracy required, since the amount of calculation goes up rapidly as greater field detail is sought. For more information on the use of numerical methods in magnetic flux calculations, reference 5 is suggested.

MAGNETIC ENERGY

To calculate the magnetic energy in a system consisting of a current-carrying conductor and magnetic media we can proceed as follows.

$$U_m = \int_0^t ei \, dt \tag{3.37}$$

where ei is the instantaneous power supplied to the system. According to Faraday's law,

$$e = N \frac{d\phi}{dt} = \frac{d\Phi}{dt} \tag{3.38}$$

where Φ represents flux linkages. Now the flux linkages within the system arise only from the source current under the assumption that $\mu(x, y, z)$ is not a function of $\mathbf{H}$. Further, with this restriction we can set

$$\Phi = Li \tag{3.39}$$

where L is a constant of proportionality.
Then

$$U_m = \int i \, d\Phi = \int Li \, di$$

or

$$U_m = \frac{1}{2} LI^2 = \frac{\Phi I}{2} \tag{3.40}$$

where I is the steady-state value of the current.

Self and Mutual Induction

The concepts of self and mutual induction in magnetically coupled systems may be defined from magnetic energy considerations. If we assume that the flux density $\mathbf{B}$ is everywhere proportional to the magnetic field strength, that is,

$$\mathbf{B} = \mu\mu_0 \mathbf{H}$$

then

$$U_m = \frac{1}{2} \sum_{k=1}^n i_k \Phi_k \tag{3.41}$$

where U_m = the energy of the field (associated with the current sources i_k). Further

$$\Phi_k = \int_{s_k} \mathbf{B} \cdot d\mathbf{s}$$

that is, ϕ_k is the magnetic flux linking the kth circuit. The symbol s_k signifies that this surface integral spans the kth circuit.

The permeability μ may be a function of position but is not to vary with $\mathbf{H}$ at a given point. The vector $\mathbf{B}$ is uniquely defined by the currents $i_1 \ldots, i_n$ and because of the stipulation that μ should be independent of $\mathbf{H}$, the contributions of the individual currents to $\mathbf{B}$ are directly proportional to their respective magnitudes.

Accordingly, we can write

$$\Phi_h = L_{h1}i_1 + L_{h2}i_2 + \cdots + L_{hn}i_n \tag{3.42}$$

Clearly L_{hk} is a geometrical factor. L_{kk} is called the self-inductance of the kth circuit, and L_{hk} is called the mutual inductance between the two circuits h and k. Now

$$L_{hk} \propto \frac{\partial \Phi_h}{\partial i_k} \tag{3.43}$$

and from equation (3.41)

$$\Phi_h \propto \frac{\partial U_m}{\partial i_h} \tag{3.44}$$

so that

$$L_{hk} \propto \frac{\partial^2 U_m}{\partial i_k \, \partial i_h} \tag{3.45}$$

Since in this relation it is immaterial in what order the subscripts appear, it follows that

$$L_{hk} = L_{kh} \tag{3.46}$$

This latter identity is very important because it permits the magnetic coupling between two circuits to be visualized in terms of the current in one and the flux linking the other or vice versa. In either case, for the same unit current in one circuit there will be the identical number of flux linkages with the second circuit, irrespective of the complexity of the circuit configuration. It is apparent in Fig. 3.6 that it would be much easier to determine the flux linking the outer coil, caused by a current through the inner loop, by using relation (3.46). In this instance the reverse problem is readily amenable to solution, since the flux density through the small inner coil, produced by current flowing

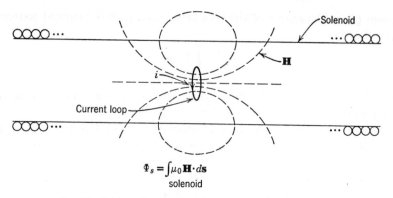

$$\Phi_s = \int_{\text{solenoid}} \mu_0 \mathbf{H} \cdot d\mathbf{s}$$

Φ_s = Flux linking solenoid due to current flow in inner loop

Fig. 3.6. Magnetic coupling between solenoid and enclosed loop.

through the large solenoid, is essentially uniform over and normal to its cross section, quite the contrary of the situation pertaining in Fig. 3.6.

MAGNETIC CIRCUITS

To obtain or sense a given field of magnetic flux in magnetic recording, specially shaped structures of ferromagnetic material are used almost exclusively. Suitable assumptions often make possible a simplification of an inherent field problem to a much simpler one involving a circuit concept. Again, in magnetic recording we are concerned only with a quasi-stationary state. Under these conditions, when the general three-dimensional magnetics problem can be reduced to a one-dimensional model for analysis, we have a so-called magnetic circuit problem.

The concept of a magnetic circuit is based on the fact that magnetic flux tends to confine itself to the high-permeability paths of a region, similar to the manner in which current flow chooses high conductivity paths in an electric circuit. However, the typical ferromagnetic circuit is characteristically non-linear.

In another important respect, the magnetic circuit differs markedly from a simple electrical equivalent. The conductivity of copper, as an example of an electrical conductor, is of the order of 10^{20} times that of a surrounding insulator material such as air or mica. In contrast, magnetic properties of materials do not vary over nearly such a wide range. Ordinarily a high-permeability substance will only have a relative permeability of 10^2 to 10^4 that of air. This condition makes flux leakage a phenomenon of major significance in magnetic circuits. Engineering applications of magnetic materials must particularly recognize and account for the behavior of leakage flux to properly relate performance to design.

Now consider Fig. 3.7, which shows a coil on an elementary magnetic toroid consisting of two sections, each with a constant but different permeability. This magnetic structure will be converted to a lumped parameter magnetic circuit to formally establish the basis and nature of the analogy to an electrical circuit.

For μ_1 and μ_2 both quite large the magnetic flux density vector $\mathbf{B}$ (within the toroid) will be essentially parallel to the surface of this ring. Now

$$\Phi = \int \mathbf{B} \cdot d\mathbf{s}$$

and for the flux within the core we then have

$$\Phi = BA \tag{3.47}$$

where A is the cross-sectional area of the magnetic path. Since B is everywhere normal to A, the vector symbolism is not necessary (again recall that the magnetic circuit represents a one-dimensional simplification of the field problem). As

$$\nabla \cdot \mathbf{B} = 0$$

the lines of flux are continuous so that Φ can be seen analogous to a current flowing around a circuit loop. Thus

$$B_1 = B_2$$

or

$$\mu_1 H_1 = \mu_2 H_2$$

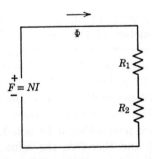

Fig. 3.7. Equivalent magnetic circuit for toroid.

H and B are parallel, and their ratio is given by the permeability constants.

Therefore if we take the line integral

$$\oint H dl$$

around the path of the magnetic ring, we obtain

$$H_1 l_1 + H_2 l_2 = Ni \tag{3.48}$$

where l_1 = arc length corresponding to μ_1
l_2 = arc length corresponding to μ_2
i = coil current (the line integral is equal to the total current encircled).

Defining, $F = Ni$ as the magnetomotive force applied to the magnetic ring, we can express the last equation in the following form:

$$F_1 + F_2 = F$$

Then, magnetomotive force (dimensionally ampere-turns) is analogous to either a voltage drop or a voltage source. The equivalence to an electric circuit may now be completed by defining

$$R = F/\Phi \tag{3.49}$$

where R is the reluctance of a given branch of the magnetic circuit. For example,

$$R_1 = \frac{F_1}{\Phi} = \frac{H_1 l_1}{BA} = \frac{l_1}{\mu_1 \mu_0 A} \tag{3.50}$$

since

$$B = \mu_1 \mu_0 H_1$$

Equation (3.50) serves also to define reluctance in terms of the parameters of the magnetic circuit. Since reluctance is the ratio of magnetomotive force to flux, it is analogous to resistance in an electrical network. It is now possible to draw the equivalent circuit as given in Fig. 3.7 and use this in solving for the magnetic behavior of the toroid. This same analogy can be directly applied to more complicated series—parallel branches in a magnetic structure.

Two points should be noted. First, in general, μ will not be a constant and therefore the reluctance of the magnetic branches will be non-linear functions. When it is essential to treat the reluctance as non-linear, recourse is necessary to graphical or numerical techniques.

Second, even in such a simple example as above one should anticipate the existence of flux leakage. In fact, for the ring of Fig. 3.7 it is only through the presence of leakage flux that we can derive a "magnetic circuit." To more readily clarify this point, assume that $\mu_1 = \mu_2$. The magnetic field intensity H is then uniform around the toroid. In the absence of the magnetic ring the line integral of H around the same path must still yield Ni. However, in the latter case the major contribution to the integral occurs on the section of the path actually traversing the coil. Thus, the magnetic field within the coil is actually reduced by the presence of the magnetic ring. This phenomenon can occur only by the existence of a "demagnetizing field" arising from equivalent magnetic poles on the surface of the toroid. These magnetic surface charges, of course, give rise to a flux outside the magnetic structure. This phenomenon exists independently of the actual permeability of the ring. A coil in a magnetic circuit actually is more appropriately equated with an induction voltage source rather than a two terminal device.

The magnetic energy of a magnetic circuit generally admits of calculation since the greater part of the magnetic flux is bounded, flowing around a one-dimensional circuit. Thus

$$U_m = \int i \, d\Phi$$

where

$$\Phi = (BA)N \tag{3.51}$$

and

$$i = \frac{Hl}{N} \tag{3.52}$$

Hence

$$U_m = V \int H \, dB$$

where $V = lA$, the volume of the region. Then,

$$u_m = \int H \, dB \tag{3.53}$$

where u_m is the magnetic energy input per unit volume associated with a change of state in B.

EDDY CURRENTS IN MAGNETIC MEDIA

Whenever the magnetic flux in a medium is changing, an electric field appears within the medium as a result of the time variation of flux.

Restating Faraday's Law, equation (3.4), with the aid of equation (3.47) and the following relation from electrostatics, we obtain

$$e = \oint_c \mathbf{E} \cdot d\mathbf{l} = \frac{\partial}{\partial t} \left[\int_s \mathbf{B} \cdot d\mathbf{s} \right] \tag{3.54}$$

where $\mathbf{E}$ is the electric field intensity.

The differential expression of the above vector field equation is

$$\nabla \times \mathbf{E} = \frac{\partial \mathbf{B}}{\partial t} \tag{3.55}$$

When the medium is a conductor, a current is set up by this induced electromotive force. These currents are called eddy currents. Their presence results in an energy loss in the material, the energy being absorbed from the source that sets up the time varying field and being dissipated as heat in the medium.

Since the permeability of ferromagnetic materials is relatively large, the effects of eddy currents on the flux density distribution and their power loss may be appreciable.

These internal currents tend to oppose any change in flux, and thus their effect is to increasingly reduce the flux density at progressively greater distances from the surface. This phenomenon is known as "skin effect." This subject is important even with non-magnetic conductors, and is treated extensively in references 5 and 6. We shall limit ourselves here to a brief development of the equation governing the behavior of the induction field B as a function of frequency for the one-dimensional problem. This situation adequately serves for a magnetic head core.

Within a conducting material

$$\mathbf{j}_t = \sigma \mathbf{E} \tag{3.56}$$

where σ is the conductivity of the material. Now substituting $\sigma \mathbf{E}$ into equation (3.15) and assuming the material has a constant permeability, we can write

$$\nabla \times \left[\frac{\mathbf{B}}{\mu \mu_0} \right] = \sigma \mathbf{E} \tag{3.57}$$

Taking the curl of both sides of this equation and using equation (3.55), we obtain

$$\nabla^2 \mathbf{B} = \mu \mu_0 \sigma \nabla \times \mathbf{E} = \mu \mu_0 \sigma \frac{\partial \mathbf{B}}{\partial t} \tag{3.58}$$

When **B** is a function of only one spatial dimension, the following differential equation gives the dependency of B on frequency f:

$$\frac{d^2B}{dx^2} = j\omega\mu\mu_0\sigma B \tag{3.59}$$

where ω (the angular frequency) $= 2\pi f$. In this particular equation, j stands for the imaginary operator of complex variable theory. B is time periodic with both amplitude and phase relations (being regarded here as varying as $e^{j\omega t}$). Equation (3.59) gives the relation between the space and time derivatives of B. To solve this equation for B, this differential equation must be subject to the boundary conditions imposed by the physical shapes under investigation.

To examine the eddy current power-loss relationships, consider a small circular cross section of radius r oriented normal to the direction of flux density in a magnetic material. Then

$$2\pi r E = \pi r^2 \frac{dB}{dt} \tag{3.60}$$

The eddy current power loss in a unit volume is proportional to E^2/ρ, where ρ is the resistivity of the material, or

$$Pe \propto \frac{1}{\rho}\left(\frac{dB}{dt}\right)^2 \tag{3.61}$$

where $Pe =$ instantaneous eddy current loss.

Thus Pe is proportional to the square of the rate of change of flux density and inversely dependent upon the resistivity. Since the induced voltage in a coil encircling the magnetic path is proportional to dB/dt, it can be deduced that

$$Pe \propto e^2 \quad (e = \text{coil voltage}) \tag{3.62}$$

This relation is frequently a useful approximation even when it is known that B is not uniform within the coil.

FERROMAGNETIC MATERIALS

Ferromagnetic behavior on a macroscopic scale may be understood through the nature of the magnetic domain substructure. An actual ferromagnetic specimen is composed of a number of small regions called domains, within each of which the atomic magnetic moments are held in parallel alignment. For this reason the domain represents a saturated region of magnetization. The directions of magnetization of different domains need not be parallel. The net magnetization of the magnetic specimen represents the integrated effect of these elemental domains.

Domain structure always has its origin in the possibility of lowering the energy of a system by going from a uniformly saturated configuration with high magnetic energy to a domain configuration with a lower energy. The domain structure is a natural consequence of the various major contributions to the total energy—exchange, anisotropy, and magnetic—of a ferromagnetic body. The interplay of these factors will be briefly sketched, for their relative influences establish the magnetic behavior of a ferromagnetic material. Further, in digital magnetic recording the recording of individually saturated magnetic cells is the means by which information bits are stored; the concepts and phenomena of domain behavior are therefore also instructive from the viewpoint of understanding digital magnetic recording.

The anisotropy energy tends to make the magnetization of a domain align itself along certain crystallographic axes. The axes thus favored are known as preferred axes, or directions of easy magnetization. A considerably larger amount of energy is generally required to saturate a specimen along an arbitrary axis than along one of the preferred axes. The non-preferred axes represent directions of "hard" magnetization. For example, in iron, which is cubic, the preferred axes are the cube edges.

The origin of domains may be understood by considering the patterns shown in Fig. 3.8. In *a* we have a saturated configuration, consisting of a single domain, which may be considered to lie along an axis of easy magnetization.

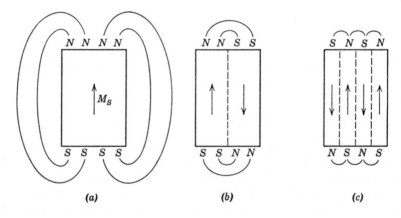

Fig. 3.8. Domain behavior—magnetostatic energy.

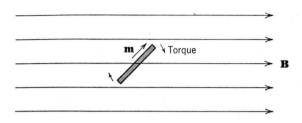

Fig. 3.9. Energy of a magnet in an external field.

The magnetostatic energy density of a permanent magnet in a uniform external field is

$$u_m = -\mathbf{M}_s \cdot \mathbf{B} \tag{3.63}$$

where $\mathbf{M}_s$ denotes the permanent magnetization. This relation may be seen by considering a small magnet of moment $\mathbf{m}$ in a magnetic field $\mathbf{B}$ (Fig. 3.9). The torque on the magnet is

$$\mathbf{m} \times \mathbf{B} \tag{3.64}$$

and the potential energy associated with its orientation can then be shown to be

$$U_m = -\mathbf{m} \cdot \mathbf{B}$$

Thus the energy is a minimum when the magnet is parallel to the field, and work is required to rotate it anti-parallel to the external field. When the field is not external but arises from the magnetization itself, the magnetostatic energy density is

$$u_m = -\tfrac{1}{2}\mathbf{M}_s \cdot \mathbf{B} \tag{3.65}$$

The factor one-half arises since equation (3.63) when applied to self-energy would effectively count each unit dipole in the assembly comprising the magnetic region once as a field source and once as a magnet in the field. The factor one-half has been encountered previously in our discussion on self- and mutual induction.

The consequence of the form of the magnetic energy expression is that the domain configuration *b* of Fig. 3.8 has approximately one-half the magnetic energy of the single domain shown in *a*. This reduction arises because of the diminution in the field throughout its spatial extension. The subdivision process may be carried further, as in *c*; here the magnetic energy is roughly one-quarter of that associated with the single domain.

The subdivision will continue, being energetically more favorable, until the energy required to establish an additional boundary (Bloch wall), separating two oppositely magnetized domains, is greater than the reduction in magnetic energy consequent on finer subdivision.

The exchange forces (quantum-mechanical) favor parallel orientation of atomic magnetic moments. These forces are non-magnetic in origin and account for the saturation magnetization condition within a domain- and hence for ferromagnetic materials. Therefore, as the magnetization is anti-parallel on opposite sides of the boundary there will be energy associated with the wall. The width of this boundary will be set by the conflicting considerations of gradual reorientation of spin moments (minimizing the exchange energy) and the fact that within the wall the directions of magnetization must necessarily reorient through a non-preferred axis of magnetization (the area here contributing anisotropy energy).

The interaction of the various energy terms will generally give rise to very complex domain patterns. An unmagnetized magnetic specimen thus consists of a somewhat randomly oriented set of domains, in a pattern minimizing the total energy.

The Magnetization Process

The increase in magnetization of a sample takes place by two independent processes: a growth of the domains favorably oriented with respect to the applied field at the expense of the unfavorably oriented domains; and rotation of the directions of magnetization toward the direction of the field. Figure 3.10 illustrates these two methods by which the resultant magnetization may change. In weak fields magnetization changes usually proceed by domain boundary displacements. In stronger fields a rotation of the direction of magnetization of the domains occurs. Figure 3.10 also shows a typical magnetization curve, designating the regions in which each process is dominant. For weak fields the boundary displacements are reversible, that is, a wall may be viewed as moving within one of a number of potential energy wells. Once the applied field causes a local energy peak (threshold) on an energy versus boundary position curve to be overcome, an irreversible boundary displacement occurs. The crystal structure, purity, etc., of the magnetic material have a pronounced influence on the magnetization process and make the physical theory very complex.

If the magnetic material is cycled by an alternating magnetic field sufficiently strong to saturate the sample, we get the familiar hysteresis loop of Fig. 3.11. The various conventional magnetic material parameters; H_c—the coercive force, B_r—the residual induction, and B_s—the saturation flux density—are defined by means of this diagram. Further, various permeability factors are given. The hysteresis loss per cycle per unit volume is equal to the area enclosed by the hysteresis loop, obtained by integrating

$$u_m = \int H \, dB$$

over a complete cycle. This hysteresis loss represents a conversion of input energy into heat within the magnetic specimen and is a result of the irreversible nature of the magnetization process.

Since

$$\mathbf{B} = \mu_0[\mathbf{H} + \mathbf{M}] \tag{3.66}$$

B will still increase proportionally to the applied field H even after saturation is reached. This will be true only for the magnetic material within the exciting coil however, for with saturation the "magnetic circuit" loses its meaning. More importantly, the conventional magnetiza-

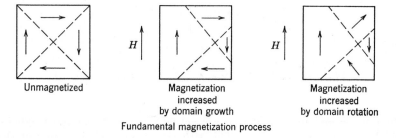

Unmagnetized   Magnetization
                      increased
                      by domain growth

          Magnetization
          increased
          by domain rotation

Fundamental magnetization process

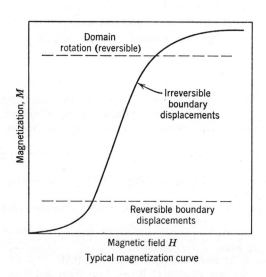

Fig. 3.10. The magnetization process.

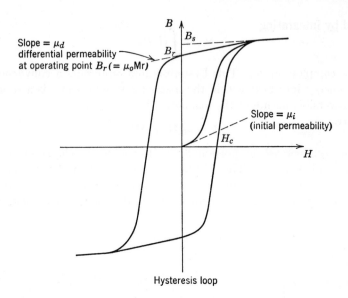

Fig. 3.11. B-H cyclic characteristic: ferromagnetic material.

tion curve and hysteresis loop are actually based on all the magnetic field vectors being parallel. This situation is not met in facets of the magnetic recording process. The highly non-linear multivalued magnetic characteristics of the materials exploited in digital magnetic recording places great demands on insight and engineering approximations to secure useful and "pseudo-optimal" design criteria.

REFERENCES

1. *Magnetism*, R. M. Bozorth, Bell Telephone System Monograph 2942, 1958.
2. *Electromagnetic Theory*, J. A. Stratton, McGraw-Hill Book Company, 1941.
3. *Classical Electricity and Magnetism*, W. K. Panofsky and M. Phillips, Addison and Wesley, 1955.
4. *Classical Electricity and Magnetism*, M. Abraham and R. Becker, Hafner Publishing Co., 1932.
5. *Magnetic Circuits and Transformers*, Staff, Electrical Engineering, MIT, John Wiley and Sons, 1943.
6. *Fields and Waves in Modern Radio*, S. Ramo and J. R. Whinnery, John Wiley and Sons, 1944.
7. *Physical Theory of Ferromagnetic Domains*, C. Kittel, Bell Telephone System Monograph 1709, 1949.
8. *Ferromagnetism*, R. M. Bozorth, Van Nostrand Co., 1951.
9. *Introduction to Solid State Physics*, C. Kittel, John Wiley and Sons, 2nd Edition, 1956.

4

THEORY OF THE DIGITAL MAGNETIC RECORDING PROCESS

In digital magnetic recording the digital (i.e., quantized) data is handled in a *binary* symbolism. The use of discrete information states makes the theory of digital magnetic recording more analogous to "transient analysis," in contrast to conventional magnetic recording theory which is concerned with frequency or wavelength response. Consequently, in a parallel with electrical circuit analyses, digital magnetic recording is most properly and effectively treated as a distinctive subject in its own right. The step function response of a magnetic recording system is the most *fundamental* descriptive characterization for digital storage.

The purpose of this chapter is to develop a useful theory and associated set of mathematical models specifically suited to digital magnetic recording. We want particularly to formulate the issues in a manner which will give insight into the basic nature of the magnetic recording process and from which valid engineering design criteria may be readily derived. For this reason the emphasis will be on concepts and explicit mathematical relations rather than on quantitive data. Digital magnetic recording performance will be clearly related to the basic parameters of the recording operation.

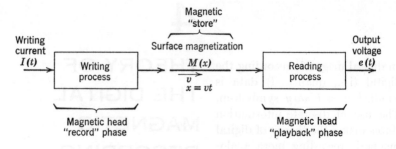

Fig. 4.1. Magnetic recording process.

Figure 4.1 shows a generalized block diagram, indicating the overall input-output transfer stages in magnetic recording. The magnetic recording process consists of two distinct operations, writing and reading. The relative motion of the storage surface provides the means by which signals in time are preserved in space, as Fig. 4.1 indicates. At some arbitrary later period of time the written information can be scanned and the stored signal recovered as a waveform in time. The relative velocity v represents the scale factor which relates the time and space domains in the recording process. Therefore, it is possible to separate independently time-dependent factors from spatially dependent factors in analyzing overall magnetic recording performance.

This chapter is devoted to the magnetic head-magnetic surface interaction phenomena in digital magnetic recording, and the next chapter treats in their individuality both magnetic head design and magnetic storage surface characterization. Great attention will be given to the issue of head-surface magnetic coupling in the digital recording process since it intrinsically establishes the storage density potential.

The theory of magnetic recording can be based on magnetostatic field theory and does not require use of the electromagnetic wave equations in their general form (Maxwell's equations). For any given recording frequency, the ratio of the recorded wavelength to the associated free space electromagnetic wavelength is given by v/c, where c is the velocity of light. Magnetic recording is concerned with spatial dimensions (for example, transducer spacing) less than or of the order of the recorded wavelengths. Thus the time necessary for propagation of electromagnetic effects (associated with the time variation of magnetization) within the head-surface coupling zone is negligible compared to the periods of magnetic field variation. Therefore we can neglect retardation phenomena and deal simply with quasi-static field relations. There may still be, of course, a measurable time lag produced by eddy currents associated with flux changes impressed on a magnetic head (Chapter 5) as well as the conventional time-dependent behavior arising from the electrical characteristics of the transducer which must be considered.

Binary recording generally dictates using two opposite senses of surface saturation to define the two unique magnetization states required. In saturation recording the write current can be easily chosen to assure consistent reproducibility of two surface states, independent of the previous history of magnetization. Therefore saturation recording is assumed in the subsequent discussions, although this assumption is not essential to the bulk of the exposition.

The subject of reading will first be considered, then the writing process. This sequence gives a better introductory perspective of the magnetic recording process. Elegance and rigour are not ends in themselves and, where warranted, will be subordinated to the twin objectives of clarity of comprehension and utility of results.

READING

Principle of Reciprocity

On reading, the magnetic field (of the surface) giving rise to flux in the magnetic head is quite small. Moreover, we are concerned here with a very high permeability core, and thus it is a valid approximation to assume that the relative permeability of the magnetic head is infinite. Therefore, it is reasonable to proceed on the basis that the *magnetic head* will act as a linear element. Further in digital magnetic recording, with each section of a track magnetized to saturation, the relative permeability of the surface medium can be considered as equal to 1.0. The magnetic medium with its magnetization distribution then appears as a "frozen" magnetic field source.

Under the conditions given, the principle of reciprocity can be very effectively applied to determine the magnetic coupling between the recording surface and the magnetic head on readback. Figure 4.2 illustrates the conventional ring-type head with a generalized picture of the magnetic field distribution setup along the recording surface when the *read coil* is energized. Since the magnetic head boundaries are magnetic equipotentials ($\mu = \infty$), it is clear that it is very much easier to determine the fringing magnetic field of the gap than to ascertain the flux from a given magnetization pattern shunted through the head core. Since γ, the head gap, is much less than the head width, b, the magnetic field pattern is effectively two-dimensional as shown. Note that contact

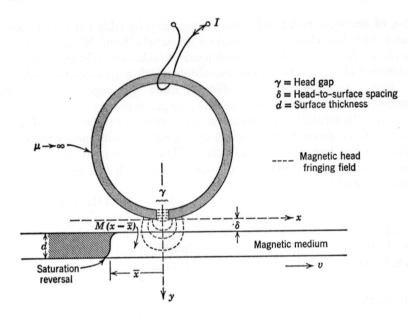

Fig. 4.2. Ring-type magnetic head, longitudinal recording.

recording may be viewed as merely a special case of non-contact recording, corresponding to setting the parameter δ equal to zero.

Knowing the magnetic head field distribution $\mathbf{H}(x)$, the flux ϕ through
an arbitrary cross section of the magnetic recording medium caused by a
current I through the read coil can be calculated. Now the reciprocity
theorem (Chapter 3) states that this same current I, encircling this cross
section of the surface medium, excites the identical flux ϕ through the
read coil on the magnetic head. If we were to replace the surface by a
set of current sources of appropriate strength, the resulting flux through
the coil of the head could then be found by summing the flux contributions from all these currents, determined in this manner.

With surface motion, the magnetization pattern $\mathbf{M}$ is continually
moving relative to the head. ($\mathbf{M}$ is the intensity of magnetization or
magnetic moment per unit volume.) Therefore $\mathbf{M} = \mathbf{M}(x - \bar{x})$ where
$\bar{x} = vt$. The variable $(x - \bar{x})$ establishes the gap centerline of the
stationary magnetic head as the frame of reference for $\mathbf{M}$. Then t (or $\bar{x}$)
equal to zero corresponds to the defined magnetization pattern being directly centered under the magnetic head. The head fringing field $\mathbf{H}(x)$ is
of course fixed with respect to x axis.

Let the head gap fringing field magnitude be considered normalized to a unit magnetomotive force (that is, **H** is defined for $NI = 1.0$, where N is the number of turns on the read coil). The fringing field of the magnetic head coupling with the surface is composed of two magnetic field components H_x and H_y. Thus, one ampere turn through the read coil would excite in an element of the magnetic surface of width b and thickness dy a differential flux.

$$d\phi_x = \mu_0 H_x b \, dy \qquad (4.1)$$

where the subscript x denotes the x-directed components. According to the reciprocity theorem, a unit current (through one turn) around the element $b \, dy$ would excite the same flux in the head read coil.

If the surface is actually magnetized with a horizontal component of magnetization $M_x(x - \bar{x})$, the magnetic moment of an element of length dx and cross section $b \, dy$ is equivalent (Chapter 3) to a current of magnitude equal to

$$M_x(x - \bar{x}) \, dx \qquad (4.2)$$

encircling the element $b \, dy$. This equivalent current represents the scale factor to be applied to equation (4.1) to adjust the latter to the actual level of the surface magnetization. The total flux through the read coil of the magnetic head caused by M_x is then obtained by integration of the differential flux contributions, arising from this magnetized pattern along the track, and is equal to

$$\phi_x(\bar{x}) = \mu_0 b \int_{y=\delta}^{\delta+d} \int_{x=-\infty}^{+\infty} M_x(x - \bar{x}, y) H_x(x, y) \, dx \, dy \qquad (4.3)$$

where d is the thickness of the recording surface and δ the spacing of the surface from the magnetic head (Fig. 4.2). ϕ_x is a function of $\bar{x}$ since the flux linking the read coil at any instant of time will depend on the corresponding location of the magnetization pattern relative to the position of the magnetic head.

In a similar manner

$$d\phi_y = \mu_0 H_y b \, dx \qquad (4.4)$$

where we now deal with a cross section in the plane of the surface, since $d\phi_y$ is by definition normal to the recording surface. Similarly, with a vertical component of magnetization M_y, the resulting magnetic moment of an element of length dy is equivalent to a current equal to

$$M_y(x - \bar{x}) \, dy \qquad (4.5)$$

encircling the element $b \, dx$.

Thus the flux linking the read coil produced by a recorded magnetization component M_y is

$$\phi_y(\bar{x}) = \mu_0 b \int_{y=\delta}^{\delta+d} \int_{x=-\infty}^{+\infty} M_y(x - \bar{x}, y) H_y(x, y) \, dx \, dy \qquad (4.6)$$

It should be noted that the two flux contributions, arising respectively from M_x and M_y, being scalar quantities, are linearly superimposed. Where only one component of magnetization exists, the behavior on reading depends *only* on the nature of the corresponding component of the magnetic head fringing field. Equations (4.3) and (4.6) represent extremely powerful tools in the analysis of the digital magnetic recording process, for they provide an effective means to deal with discontinuous and non-periodic magnetization patterns.

Idealized Ring Head

An idealized ring head is shown in Fig. 4.3. The pole faces in this structure are parallel to the recording surface, and they are assumed to extend to infinity. Again, the permeability of the magnetic head core is

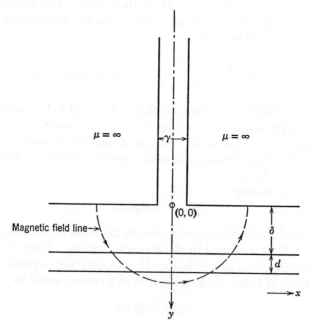

Fig. 4.3. Idealized ring head.

assumed to be infinite. This convenient model is usually a valid representation for many magnetic heads, and therefore results obtained using it are of wide general interest. In particular, it permits analytical means to be applied to calculate the relative influence of the various spatial parameters encountered in the magnetic recording process.

A precise analytic solution of the idealized ring head fringing field is not obtainable in explicit form, and the equations involved are quite complicated, even though the geometry is simple. The horizontal fringing field component is of primary importance, since in writing with a ring head longitudinal magnetization is predominant. Now an analytical expression [Karlquist (4)] has been obtained for the fringing field component $H_x(x, y)$ of an idealized ring head by assuming a linear magnetic potential gradient across the gap at the plane $y = 0$ (Fig. 4.3). This expression gives a very close approximation for this fringing field component of an idealized ring head. Indeed, typically, further simplifications are usually made for given regions of the gap fringing field. This freedom results from: (a) only relatively coarse control can be exercised in magnetic recording over the precision, stability, and reproducibility of a complete recording system; and (b) the possibilities for precise instrumentation and consequently detailed experimental interaction with theory are severely limited. Engineering design, of course, must strike a proper balance between theory and practice.

From Karlquist,

$$H_x(x, y) = \frac{H_g}{\pi} \left[\tan^{-1}\left(\frac{\gamma/2 + x}{y}\right) + \tan^{-1}\left(\frac{\gamma/2 - x}{y}\right) \right] \quad (4.7)$$

where H_g is the magnetic field within the gap of the idealized ring head. With the magnitude of H normalized to a unit magnetomotive force, H_g can be replaced in the above and following equations by $1/\gamma$ since the only section of the magnetic head circuit that has a magnetic potential gradient is the gap.

The maximum horizontal field intensity for a given value of y will occur along the plane $x = 0$. Then, the equation giving the dependency of $H_x|_{max}$ upon $y(y > 0)$ is

$$H_x(0, y) = \frac{2}{\pi\gamma} \tan^{-1}\left(\frac{\gamma/2}{y}\right) \quad (4.8)$$

For $y \gg \gamma/2$ (γ = gap size) this equation can be simplified to

$$H_x(0, y) = \frac{1}{\pi y} \quad (4.9)$$

Thus at large values of y the fringing field strength drops off inversely with spacing.

For the plane $y = 0$, from equation (4.7)

$$H_x(x, 0) = \begin{cases} 0 & |x| > \gamma/2 \\ 1/\gamma & |x| < \gamma/2 \end{cases}$$

recalling that $\tan^{-1}$ is an odd function and $\tan^{-1}(\infty) = \pi/2$. This result corresponds to the field right along the pole faces and, of course, just represents a check with the basic assumptions upon which equation (4.7) was derived.

A region where we can obtain a simplified formulation of $H_x(x)$ is along y planes (distant from the head) for which $y > \gamma$. While this relation can be obtained by mathematical manipulations, using equation (4.7), it is much more instructive to deduce the form of H_x by a geometrical consideration of the field of Fig. 4.3, under the equivalence condition that γ approaches zero. Then the magnetic equipotential lines subdividing the region between the external pole faces become radial. The magnetic field lines are semicircles and also lines of constant magnetic field strength. Thus,

$$H = \frac{1}{\pi r}$$

where $r^2 = x^2 + y^2$ (using the line integral equation relating H and its source current).

Therefore

$$H_x = H \frac{y}{r} = \frac{1}{\pi y} \left(\frac{1}{1 + u^2} \right) \tag{4.10}$$

where $u = x/y$. This equation for H_x is identical with the field that would be obtained from a "filamentary" wire current source placed at the gap origin $x = y = 0$ in place of the idealized ring head.

In the approximation just given, the parameter γ no longer appears in the field equation. This is equivalent to considering γ negligible compared to the other spatial factors. Even so, for $y > \gamma$ the resulting error is small, and equation (4.10) thus represents a particularly simple and useful analytical expression for H_x for purposes of theoretical analyses of magnetic recording behavior.

Sine Wave Magnetization

The first form of surface magnetization to be considered will be sinusoidal. This approach will best convey the general applicability of the concepts being developed. In particular, the conventional wavelength response dependency on spatial parameters will be derived. These relations are fundamental to audio magnetic recording, and this section will not only indicate the compatibility of this theoretical approach with conventional sine wave analysis but may give additional insight into the nature of the wavelength factors themselves to those only familiar with the frequency response method of treatment of magnetic recording.

Let M_x be uniform throughout the recording layer, and let us set $M_x = M_r \cos k(x - \bar{x})$, where $k = 2\pi/\lambda$. λ = recorded wavelength. Then, from equation (4.3)

$$\phi = M_r \mu_0 b \int_{\delta}^{\delta+d} dy \int_{-\infty}^{+\infty} \cos k(x - \bar{x}) H_x(x, y) \, dx \qquad (4.11)$$

The so-called gap loss describes the reduction in short-wavelength resolution caused by the finite size of the head gap. This "aperture" effect is obviously a more pronounced factor in performance as the gap size γ becomes larger relative to δ and d. If we first consider $\delta \to 0$ and $d \to 0$, the head gap becomes the sole factor in setting performance. Under these assumptions we can, as demonstrated previously, approximate H_x by

$$H_x = \begin{cases} 0 & x < -\gamma/2 \\ 1/\gamma & -\gamma/2 < x < \gamma/2 \\ 0 & x > \gamma/2 \end{cases}$$

For convenience, we will set $K = M_r \mu_0 b$. Furthermore,

$$M_r \cos k(x - \bar{x}) = M_r[\cos kx \cos \omega t + \sin kx \sin \omega t] \qquad (4.12)$$

since

$$k\bar{x} = \frac{2\pi vt}{\lambda} = \omega t$$

ω is the recorded frequency in radians per second. Since $\sin kx$ is an odd function, the $\sin kx$ term in equation (4.12) will make no contribution to the integral in expression (4.11), with the given H_x function. Therefore,

$$\phi = \frac{K}{\gamma} \int_{\delta}^{\delta+d} dy \int_{-\gamma/2}^{+\gamma/2} \cos kx \, dx [\cos \omega t] \qquad (4.13)$$

or

$$\phi = Kd \frac{\sin (\pi\gamma/\lambda)}{(\pi\gamma/\lambda)} [\cos \omega t] \qquad (4.14)$$

Equation (4.14) gives the well-known standard gap loss function, $\sin (\pi\gamma/\lambda)/(\pi\gamma/\lambda)$. It can be seen that this particularly simple flux-wavelength relation would not be expected to apply, other than as a rough approximation, in the general recording environment. $\lambda = \gamma$ corresponds to a point of infinite attenuation (zero output, since the head flux is then zero). Points of infinite attenuation also are predicted at all wavelengths which are submultiples of the gap width. We note that the read coil flux is directly proportional to d (recall that this case corresponds to both d and δ much smaller than γ, in accord with the approximation for H_x). A derivation of the gap loss factor under less restrictive assumptions has been made [by Westmijze (3)], which results principally in slightly adjusted values of the null-point wavelengths.

We have seen that there is another fringing field region for which we can get a simple analytical formulation of H_x, that is, for $y > \gamma$. From equation (4.10)

$$H_x = \frac{1}{\pi y}\left(\frac{1}{1 + u^2}\right)$$

Again H_x is an even function in x and hence the expansion of $\cos k(x - \bar{x})$ will result in a reading flux contribution arising only from the term $\cos kx \cos \omega t$. Therefore we can write

$$\phi = \frac{K}{\pi}\int_{\delta}^{\delta+d} dy \int_{-\infty}^{+\infty} \frac{\cos (ky)u}{1 + u^2}\, du[\cos \omega t] \qquad (4.15)$$

as $dx = y\, du$.

Since $\cos (ky)u$ is an even function in u, we can change the limits of integration of u from 0 to ∞ and double the answer so obtained.

Now

$$\int_0^{\infty} \frac{\cos ax}{1 + x^2}\, dx = \frac{\pi}{2}\, e^{-a}, a > 0 \qquad (4.16)$$

So

$$\phi = K\int_{\delta}^{\delta+d} e^{-ky}\, dy[\cos \omega t] \qquad (4.17)$$

Solving for ϕ, we obtain

$$\phi = K\left(\frac{1 - e^{-2\pi d/\lambda}}{2\pi d/\lambda}\right)(e^{-2\pi\delta/\lambda})\,[\cos \omega t] \qquad (4.18)$$

The factors describing the influence of recording medium thickness, d, and the spacing between head and surface, δ, occur separately. The importance of the spacing on the short-wavelength response is evidenced by the exponential attenuation factor within which the spacing variable appears. Further, as $d/\lambda \to 0$, ϕ becomes proportional to the medium thickness d, while as $d/\lambda \to \infty$, the amplitude of the reading coil flux becomes independent of the parameter d.

Step Function Change in Magnetization

The actual signal we obtain on readback is a voltage, proportional to the time derivative of flux through the read coil. We are particularly interested in the waveform of the voltage pulse produced for a step function change in magnetization, since any pattern of magnetization changes made up of alternations between two discrete states can be resolved into a unique series of step functions. Then the output voltage for a given binary input signal can be synthesized from a single standard waveform response. Therefore we shall first extend equation (4.3) to obtain a general expression for the read coil voltage.

Since

$$e_x(vt) = e_x(\bar{x}) = vN \frac{d\phi_x}{d\bar{x}} \qquad (4.19)$$

we can write

$$e_x(\bar{x}) = KvN \int_{\delta}^{\delta+d} dy \int_{-\infty}^{+\infty} \frac{\partial M_x(x - \bar{x})}{\partial \bar{x}} H_x(x, y) \, dx \qquad (4.20)$$

We express e_x as a function of $\bar{x}$ since the output voltage is inherently related to a distance measure rather than absolute time. As $\bar{x} = vt$, v is a scale factor for the output voltage both in time (pulse width) and in amplitude as indicated by equation (4.19). The integral in equation (4.20) is a convolution integral, and therefore H_x can be thought of as a "weighting" function.

Let us now consider the case where $M_y = 0$ and we have a step function change in horizontal magnetization M_x from $-M_r$ to $+M_r$ throughout the recording medium (see Fig. 4.2, for example). We will not initially place any restraints on the spatial parameters.

Now for the problem under consideration

$$\frac{\partial M_x(x - \bar{x})}{\partial \bar{x}} \equiv M_x'(x - \bar{x}) = 2M_r \, \delta(x - \bar{x}) \qquad (4.21)$$

where $\delta(x - \bar{x})$ is the unit impulse or delta function. Then, substituting in equation (4.20), we find

$$e(\bar{x}) = e_x(\bar{x}) \propto \int_{\delta}^{\delta+d} H_x(\bar{x}, y) \, dy \qquad (4.22)$$

the various constants being omitted to give maximum focus on perhaps the most significant relation in digital (or pulse) magnetic recording. Equation (4.22) provides a direct means of predicting the shape of the output pulse from a step change in magnetization, knowing the coupling fringing field of the magnetic head. This expression is applicable to any magnetic head structure, although an estimate for H_x is essential. H_x may be determined either analytically, graphically, numerically, or experimentally, depending on the suitability of a given method for the complexity of the problem. If there was also a vertical component of magnetization present, its output voltage contribution would directly add algebraically to the above signal.

For $d/\delta \to 0$

$$e(\bar{x}) \propto d \cdot H_x(\bar{x}, \delta) \tag{4.23}$$

Equation (4.23) states that if the ratio d/δ is small the output voltage waveform in time will resemble the static field distribution of the head H_x along the plane of the recording medium (distant δ from the head) and its amplitude will be proportional to d.

Again, returning to the case where $\delta > \gamma$, we can rewrite equation (4.10) as follows:

$$H_x \propto \frac{y}{r^2} = \frac{y}{x^2 + y^2} \tag{4.24}$$

and therefore

$$e(\bar{x}) \propto \int_{\delta}^{\delta+d} \frac{y \, dy}{\bar{x}^2 + y^2} = \ln\left[\frac{\bar{x}^2 + (\delta + d)^2}{\bar{x}^2 + \delta^2}\right] \tag{4.25}$$

When $d/\delta \to 0$ we may set $y = \delta$ in equation (4.24), and by substituting (4.24) in equation (4.23) we obtain

$$e(\bar{x}) \propto \frac{d/\delta}{1 + (\bar{x}/\delta)^2} \tag{4.26}$$

Equation (4.26) very directly evidences the manner in which the spatial parameters affect the output pulse amplitude and pulse shape when the head-to-surface spacing is the dominant parameter.

Furthermore,

$$\frac{e(\bar{x})}{e(0)} = \frac{1}{1 + (\bar{x}/\delta)^2} \tag{4.27}$$

where $e(0) = e_{\text{peak}}$. If we measure the pulse width at the points where the relative amplitude of the pulse is down to 10% of its peak value we find

$$|(\bar{x}/\delta)| \approx 3.0 \tag{4.28}$$

or the pulse width η is equal to six times the head-to-surface spacing.

Figure 4.4 illustrates the character of output signal that would be obtained from a step change in horizontal magnetization along a differential recording layer, when located at progressively larger distances from the

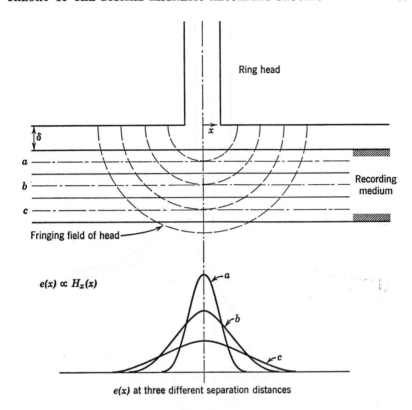

$e(x)$ at three different separation distances

Fig. 4.4. Step response output signals.

head. The waveforms are identical with the fringing field component H_x at these same spacings. For the overall recording surface indicated, the net output pulse may be approximated to a fair degree by the linear addition of the component signals produced by the three strata shown. The farther a given stratum is from the magnetic head, the smaller its corresponding output signal amplitude and the broader its pulse width. For highest pulse resolution a very thin surface is therefore required, unless it is practicable to use non-saturation recording techniques which can confine the magnetized layer to the upper section of the surface. In either case, increasing pulse resolution means the acceptance of an appreciable reduction in pulse amplitude. These approaches to improvement in pulse resolution (reduction in the effective recording layer thickness) will be only important when there results a significant decrease in the quantity $\delta + d$.

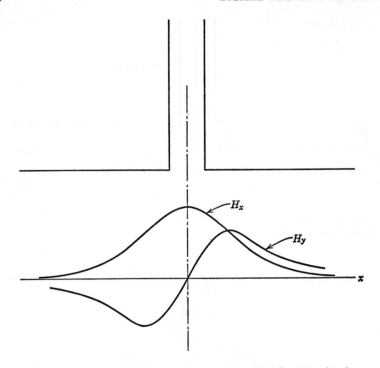

Fig. 4.5. H_x and H_y at fixed distance y from idealized ring head.

Figure 4.5 gives curves of H_x and H_y for the idealized ring head. It is seen that the output signal from a step change in vertical magnetization will be a dipulse. Any significant degree of vertical magnetization will result in considerable pulse distortion because of the nature of this contribution to the total output signal. On the other hand, the difference in response between e_x and e_y provides a means to determine the general character of the surface magnetization. It is found that with ring heads it is generally adequate to assume that the resultant magnetization is entirely horizontal. Thus great attention is given in the design of the magnetic head configuration to narrow the H_x coupling function of the recording system. This type of improvement is directly translated into a higher pulse resolution. In the next chapter, in addition to gap width, factors such as the shaping of pole tips, coil location, etc., will be considered, for they can contribute to a narrowing of the coupling function H_x, over a specified range of head-to-surface spacing.

Finite Transition Width in the Change of Magnetization. In practice we would not actually expect to record true step changes in magnetization. Here we shall consider how the output pulse is modified if the change in magnetization from $-M_r$ to $+M_r$ occurs over a distance x_1 in a uniform manner. Again, we assume H_x does not vary over d; thus H_x is not a function of y.

Then (Fig. 4.6)

$$M_x = -M_r \qquad\qquad x \leq \bar{x}$$

$$M_x = -M_r + \frac{2M_r x}{x_1} \qquad \bar{x} \leq x \leq \bar{x} + x_1$$

$$M_x = +M_r \qquad\qquad x \geq \bar{x} + x_1$$

and

$$M_x'(x - \bar{x}) = \frac{-2M_r(x - \bar{x})}{x_1} \qquad (4.29)$$

for

$$\bar{x} \leq x \leq \bar{x} + x_1$$

and is equal to zero otherwise. Substituting into equation (4.20), we obtain

$$e(\bar{x}) \propto \frac{\displaystyle\int_{\bar{x}}^{\bar{x}+x_1} H_x(x)\,dx}{x_1} \qquad (4.30)$$

This expression is seen to agree with our earlier analysis in the limit as $x_1 \to 0$. Equation (4.30) may be interpreted as follows. $e(\bar{x})$ is obtained by averaging H_x over the distance x_1 for all values of $\bar{x}$. The transition width x_1 has the effect of reducing the signal peak and increasing the pulse width. To a first-order approximation the pulse width will be increased by the amount x_1 over that obtained from a true recorded step change, and the pulse amplitude will be correspondingly reduced

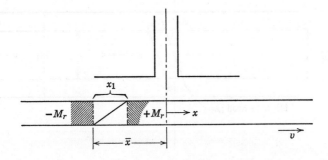

Fig. 4.6. Model for finite width of magnetization reversal.

in the same degree. Normally x_1 is considerably less than the spread of H_x along the track (by a factor of 5 to 10), and therefore the step function approximation for a magnetization change is quite good.

Azimuth Alignment

Since in magnetic recording we have essentially a two-dimensional magnetic fringing field, each incremental strip of track width couples independently with the section of the head in its plane. So far it has been presumed that the magnetic head gap is perfectly aligned normal to the recording track, so that the recorded magnetization pattern traversing across each differential slice of the head gap on reading is identical at every instant. In practice, some misalignment between the recorded pattern and head gap can arise because of the inability to mechanically achieve a perfectly stable recording system. We shall calculate in this section the manner in which this azimuth misalignment influences the output signal and consequently the performance.

The simplest way to formulate this problem is by regarding the magnetic head as composed of a set of read elements of differential width operating in parallel, whose output signals are added together. This viewpoint merely corresponds to the fact that the net flux (and hence voltage output) of a magnetic head is directly proportional to its width.

Now let ψ be the angle between the line of the head gap and a line normal to the recording track; let b be the width of the read head; and W be the width of the recorded track (Fig. 4.7). We shall consider the problem in its most general form, where b can be either less than or greater than W.

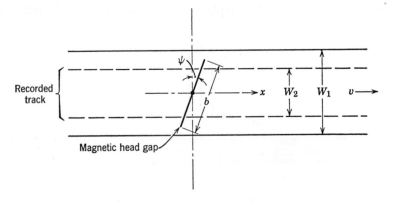

Fig. 4.7. Azimuth alignment.

(a) $b < W$ $(W = W_1$ in Fig. 4.7)

For this case, the net flux intercepted by the magnetic head is set by b. If $e(\bar{x})$ is the output voltage when $\psi = 0$, then db/b is the fraction of the net output voltage contributed by each differential head section db. Then for $\psi \neq 0$

$$e(\bar{x}) = \int_{-b\cos\psi/2}^{b\cos\psi/2} e(\bar{x} - x)\,\frac{db}{b} \qquad (4.31)$$

since the voltage signal from each differential section is slightly offset from that arising from the center of the magnetic head. The "intercept" cross section of the head is $b\cos\psi$, which establishes the above limits for the integral. Now

$$db = dx/\sin\psi \qquad (4.32)$$

where the corresponding limits in terms of x are $\pm \dfrac{b\sin\psi}{2}$. Therefore

$$e(\bar{x}) = \frac{1}{b\sin\psi} \int_{-b\sin\psi/2}^{b\sin\psi/2} e(\bar{x} - x)\,dx \qquad (4.33)$$

It is recognized in this form that the output signal is affected by the misalignment (ψ) in a manner similar to that caused by a finite magnetization reversal region (x_1). Thus any azimuth misalignment will result in a spread of the pulse width and a reduction in its amplitude. Furthermore, $b\sin\psi$ should be much less than η (the pulse width for a step change in magnetization) if no loss of pulse resolution is to occur.

(b) $b > W$ $(W = W_2$ in Fig. 4.7)

In this case the flux intercepted by the magnetic head is set by W. It is only necessary here to replace $b\sin\psi$ by $W\tan\psi$ in the previous equation. This results from the fact that rather than db/b we have dW/W for the fractional contribution of each differential section of the track to the output. Now

$$dW = dx/\tan\psi$$

and the limits for x will now be $\pm(W\tan\psi)/2$, corresponding to the limits of $\pm W/2$ for the effective "cross section" of the magnetic head.

To show the correlation of this analysis with the more familiar sine wave theory, let us take as an example

$$b > W$$

and

$$e(\bar{x}) = \cos k\bar{x} \qquad (\psi = 0)$$

where $k = 2\pi/\lambda$. Then from equation (4.12) and the fact that here also the sine term obtained from equation (4.12) will make no contribution to the voltage integral (equation 4.33), we obtain

$$e(\bar{x}) = \left(\frac{1}{W \tan \psi} \int_{-W \tan \psi/2}^{W \tan \psi/2} \cos kx \, dx \right) \cos k\bar{x} \qquad (4.34)$$

or

$$e(\bar{x}) \propto \frac{\sin \left(\dfrac{\pi W \tan \psi}{\lambda} \right)}{\left(\dfrac{\pi W \tan \psi}{\lambda} \right)} \qquad (4.35)$$

which is the conventional expression for the azimuth alignment factor in audio magnetic recording.

Voltage Waveform Characteristics

The basic signal characteristic is an output pulse for a step change in horizontal magnetization. The peak of the voltage pulse is coincident with the passage of the magnetization step change by the center of the head gap, and its duration is given by the time required for the step change to traverse the coupling horizontal fringing field of the magnetic head gap. Changing the speed of relative motion will proportionately change the pulse amplitude and inversely change the pulse width. Since a step reversal in saturation represents the maximum change in surface magnetization possible, the associated output pulse gives the peak readback amplitude obtainable. Furthermore, in binary recording the two states of magnetization must alternate; therefore the output voltage from a recorded pattern must be alternating in character.

The principles developed here apply equally well to either horizontal or vertical magnetization. To predict recording performance, it is absolutely essential to have an adequate picture of the reading head fringing field. The relation between magnetic head structure and its fringing field distribution will be undertaken in the next chapter. Usually, however, the idealized ring head serves as an adequate model for rough design analysis.

Another fundamental property of the fringing field H_x (or the output voltage pulse) may be seen by reference to Fig. 4.8. Shown by dotted line is an integration path from one pole piece of a magnetic head to the other. We know that the line integral $\int \mathbf{H} \cdot d\mathbf{l} = 1.0$ for any path chosen, based on our definition of $\mathbf{H}$ and the fact that we have assumed the ring

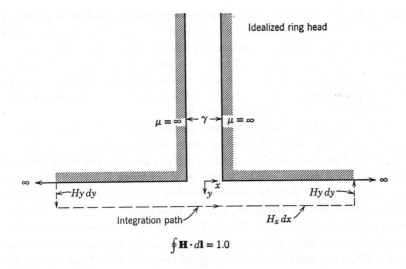

Fig. 4.8. Selected path of line integral of fringing field.

head core to be of infinite permeability. For the particular path chosen as the vertical path legs approach infinity, their contribution to the integral becomes negligible. Therefore,

$$\int_{-\infty}^{+\infty} H_x \, dx = 1.0 \tag{4.36}$$

This is an exceedingly useful relation, since we already have derived an equation for the amplitude of $H_x(0, y)$, that is, equation (4.8). We are able to state a great deal about the general fringing field without any real computation. We know that: (a) the integral of the function $H_x(x)$ is constant, independent of the value of y; (b) we have a relation for $H_x|_{\max}$ versus y; and (c) H_x is symmetrical about $x = 0$ for a symmetrical head structure.

Geometrical scaling is an important design tool. For example, with an idealized ring head, if we reduce both γ and δ by a factor of 2 (d being quite small), the resulting fringing field function is identical, merely being scaled down dimensionally by a factor of 2. Thus, in this instance, the output pulse width would be halved. Further,

$$N \, \Delta\phi_x = \int_{-\infty}^{+\infty} e(\bar{x}) \, d\bar{x} \propto \int_{-\infty}^{+\infty} H_x(x) \, dx = 1.0 \tag{4.37}$$

where $\Delta\phi_x$ is the net change in flux through the read coil as a result of reading a step change in horizontal magnetization. Thus we could also expect the pulse amplitude to double, which is necessary to preserve the integral relation just given. The reason so much emphasis is placed on the reduction of dimensions as a means to higher and higher density performance is clearly evidenced from the consequences of geometrically scaling down the coupling fringing field.

In practice, the output signal may be modified by the time constants of the read coil. While the voltage pulse is rising towards its peak, the distributed parameters of the reading coil are acquiring or being charged with electrical energy. (The source of this energy is actually the mechanical drive causing the relative motion between surface and head.) During the fall-off of the pulse, a decay time is necessary for the dissipation of this stored energy. The influence of the coil constants depends on the basic exciting pulse shape; in general, the time constants of the coil will tend to make the trailing edge of the pulse fall off more gradually than the leading edge rises. The electrical characteristics of a magnetic head (and its terminating impedance) as they relate to pulse recording is a subject included in Chapter 5.

WRITING

In digital magnetic recording, one design goal for writing performance is to achieve (as closely as possible) a true step change in magnetization upon switching the direction of writing current. Further, successive changes in writing current should have no effect on the region of the surface just recorded. Under these conditions there would exist no limitation on the density of saturation magnetization reversals that could be recorded, and the performance of the magnetic recording system would then be set entirely by the characteristics of the reading operation.

Step Change in Write Current

No widely accepted analysis relating the magnetization transition width to the recording head geometry, writing current, and magnetic properties of the recording medium has been yet developed. The physics is complicated not only by the highly non-linear nature of the problem but also by the fact that the individual magnetic surface regions are actually acted upon by a time varying vector field as they leave the vicinity of the magnetic head.

The following graphical model is offered as giving an intuitive understanding of the write process and as being suitable for design guides in
terms of the recording system parameters. H_x is considered constant
over the recording depth.

For a step-like change in the magnetizing field, only the surface region
under the trailing leg half of the magnetic head need be considered
(Fig. 4.9). All the magnetic regions of the track passing the head gap
centerline traverse the same magnetizing field and hence will be uniformly saturated. By the graphical procedure illustrated in Fig. 4.10, it
is possible to construct a curve of $M_x(x)$.

Before application of a current change, the surface is being uniformly
saturated. Assuming an instantaneous reversal in the writing field, the
resultant magnetizing field is graphically projected on the recording
medium magnetization characteristic to yield the resultant curve for the
recorded transition zone. At the gap center, H_x is sufficient to completely reverse the direction of saturation. The magnetizing field dimin-
ishes with x (direction of motion) until, when projected on the "demagnetization curve" of the magnetic surface material, no modification of
the existing saturation state occurs. Each surface point on the trailing
leg side of the head gap is exposed to the maximum magnetizing field,
tending to reverse its direction of saturation, at the initial instant
of switching. As an elemental volume leaves the region of the head, it

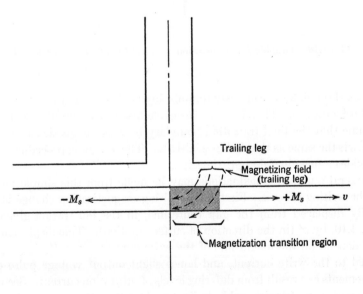

Fig. 4.9. Idealized ring head: saturation reversal.

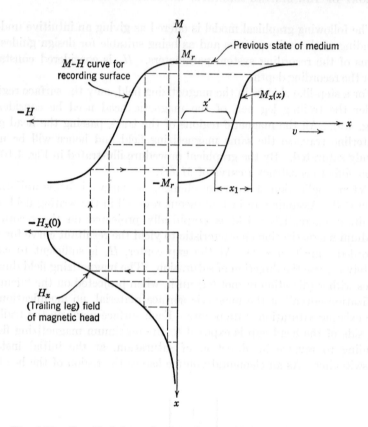

Fig. 4.10. Graphical determination of $M_x(x)$ for a saturation reversal.

passes through a continuously diminishing field (having a constant general orientation). Therefore, a reasonable first-order simplification is to assume that the final transition boundary between magnetic saturation states is the same as that holding initially. The foregoing procedure then provides a meaningful approximation.

Several qualitative deductions may be made from this simple model of the writing process. First, the resulting magnetization change is actually displaced from the gap centerline, in the illustration given in Fig. 4.10, by x' (in the direction of surface motion). This displacement will depend on the magnitude of the write current, since H_x is proportional to the write current, and hence slight output voltage pulse displacements can result from differing levels of saturation current. Second, the greater the fringing field gradient and/or the more rectangular the magnetic properties of the storage medium, the closer will the magnetization transition width approach a true step. Third, it can be seen that the actual size of the writing gap will not have a sensitive influence on the recorded magnetization change. At a given spacing δ, the gap proper primarily influences H_x only in the central part of the coupling zone.

The actual transition width x_1 is difficult to measure. In Fig. 4.10, x_1 is taken as the distance between the 10% to 90% saturation change points. This transition width is considerably less than the width of the fringing field coupling zone. This fact is indicated in Fig. 4.10, by comparing the curve of M_x with H_x. This result is seen to be a consequence of the non-linear saturation characteristic of the magnetic storage medium. The output pulse from a step change is proportional to H_x (equation 4.23), and therefore in practice the output signal will not differ significantly from that determined on the basis of a perfect step change in saturation. Experimental data tend to place the actual saturation transition width at 20% or less of the output pulse width (9).

Whenever the surface magnetization is being reversed, a magnetization reversal will exist on the leading leg side of the magnetic head. The magnetization transitions so established on the leading edge of the gap are immediately eradicated as they pass by the gap centerline, with continuous current writing. Thus, a special case arises when the write current is turned off. A signal will result from any magnetization change recorded by the leading edge of the write gap. Should a pulsed write current be used, the output from a single current pulse will be two voltage pulses displaced in time (by approximately $2x'/v$ plus the time of duration of the current pulse) and of reverse polarity (since, for example, the surface magnetization will go from zero to $+M_r$ and back again to zero). The output signal is then a dipulse.

Writing Density

In addition to taking cognizance of the saturation transition width, there is the associated question of the density at which such step-like changes can be recorded. To preserve a step-like change just written, the surface should move at least a distance x_1 before another magnetization change is initiated. This displacement will move that edge of the transition region, which has just been saturated in the reverse sense at the gap center, out beyond the range of the effective magnetizing field (for a saturated region). Since the reading process imposes a more severe limitation on performance than does the writing, we find that this restriction on writing rate is not approached in practice.

Thus, while the ideal writing conditions cannot be met, it is generally found that the reading operation primarily establishes the overall input-output transfer characteristic of the digital magnetic recording process.

REFERENCES

1. "Signal and Noise Levels in Magnetic Tape Recording," D. E. Wooldridge, *AIEE Transactions*, Vol. 65, pp. 343–52, June 1948.
2. "The Reproduction of Magnetically Recorded Signals," R. L. Wallace, *Bell System Technical Journal*, October 1951.
3. "*Studies on Magnetic Recording*," W. K. Westmijze, Philips Research Laboratories, Report R 213, 214, 217, 222, 1953.
4. "Calculation of the Magnetic Field in the Ferromagnetic Layer of a Magnetic Drum," O. Karlquist, Trans. Royal Inst. of Tech., Stockholm, Sweden, No. 86, 1954.
5. "Magnetic Data Recording Theory: Head Design," A. S. Hoagland, *Communication and Electronics (AIEE)*, pp. 506–513, November 1956.
6. "On the Resolving Power in the Process of Magnetic Recording," S. Duinker, *Tijdschrift van het Nederlands Radiogenootschap*, pp. 29–48, January 1957.
7. "The Recording and Reproduction of Signals on Magnetic Medium Using Saturation-Type Recording," J. J. Miyata and R. R. Hartel, *Transactions of the IRE-PGEC*, Vol. EC8, pp. 159–168, June 1959.
8. "Determination of the Recording Performance of a Tape from its Magnetic Properties," E. D. Daniel, A. Levine, *Journal of the Acoustical Society of America*, Vol. 32, No. 2, pp. 258–267, February 1960.
9. "Magnetic Recording and Reproduction of Pulses," D. F. Eldridge, *IRE National Convention Record*, March 1960.

5

This chapter is concerned with the design factors associated individually with the magnetic head and the magnetic recording surface. Principal emphasis will be given to those facets that are unique to the art of magnetic recording. The magnetic head interaction with the magnetic surface occurs through that region of the gap fringing field intercepted by (or coupled to) the manetic track. Therefore in the treatment of magnetic heads the two spatial parameters δ and d (head-to-surface spacing and surface thickness respectively), which together define the location of the surface with respect to the head, must necessarily be included. Surface thickness is thus the one common parameter the discussions on magnetic heads and storage media will have.

This chapter covers first the subject of magnetic heads and then that of magnetic media. In digital magnetic recording, transducer *area* resolution and surface potential in density of discrete saturation states become of particular interest. No attempt is made to document design details or specifications; rather, design procedures and design guides are given. The work presented here builds on the theory developed in the preceding chapters.

MAGNETIC HEADS AND STORAGE MEDIA

MAGNETIC HEADS—MAGNETIC ASPECTS

Although three modes of recording were mentioned in Chapter 1, longitudinal recording (using a ring-type head) is almost exclusively used. Therefore the analyses presented here will be confined to this category of magnetic recording structure. The general principles set forth, however, are equally valid and applicable to the other modes of recording (vertical and transverse).

The magnetic head is fabricated from some "soft" magnetic material. Briefly, restating the *magnetic* properties desired for a magnetic head core: (1) a high-saturation flux density to assure saturation of the recording medium on writing; (2) a high initial permeability to maximize the magnetic coupling between read coil and surface on readback; and (3) negligible residual induction so the continued presence of the head when inoperative will not affect a previously recorded signal. Further, the frequency response of the head should extend high enough to avoid frequency limitations on performance. (Thus, in practice, laminations from $\frac{1}{2}$ to 2 mils in thickness, or ferrite materials, are generally used for core construction.)

Gap Fringing Field—General

The importance of the magnetic head fringing field has been stressed previously. This field distribution not only magnetizes the surface on writing but in digital magnetic recording also sets the basic pulse shape and signal resolution on reading. The configuration of the magnetic pole pieces, in conjunction with the size of the gap, establishes the predominant character of the magnetic head fringing field. Our frame of reference will be the idealized magnetic ring head which has been illustrated again in Fig. 5.1. A magnetic head, whose pole faces extend parallel to the plane of the recording surface for a distance many times greater than the largest parameter among spacing, gap size, and surface thickness, may be approximated by an idealized ring head. Therefore, while the poles of the idealized ring head model extend to infinity, this model serves as an excellent representation of a large number of practical devices.

The gap dimension γ is always much less than the head width b. This fact is the result of practical considerations involved in the head-surface geometry. The head output signal is proportional to b, and the greater the track width the more effectively averaged out are noise signals from minute surface defects. Further, coil size and head mounting requirements impose restrictions on the proximity of tracks. If lateral head

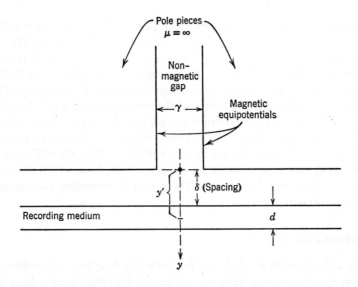

Fig. 5.1. Idealized ring head.

positioning devices are used, their mechanical tolerances provide other restraints on track density. Therefore, we typically find gaps in the order of 100 microinches associated with head widths ranging from 100 to 1000 times this magnitude. Thus, the gap fringing field can be represented as a two-dimensional magnetic field distribution. Consequently the magnetic design of a head configuration is effectively a two-dimensional field problem.

As mentioned, in analyzing the idealized ring head we need a means of incorporating the factors of head-to-surface spacing and recording medium thickness. For this purpose, the parameter

$$y' = \delta + d/2 \tag{5.1}$$

will be introduced. y' is the distance from the magnetic head to the midplane of the recording medium (see Fig. 5.1). The actual magnetic coupling between the head and surface at a given plane x is given by

$$\int_{\delta}^{\delta+d} \mathbf{H}(x, y) \, dy \tag{5.2}$$

where $\mathbf{H}$ is the magnetic head fringing field (Chapter 4). We can correctly consider d as the recording surface thickness in saturation recording; in non-saturation binary recording, the parameter d should be viewed as a measure of the effective surface layer penetration of the magnetizing field. The definition of y' will permit a single field distribution, $\mathbf{H}(x, y')$, to be used as an "average value" approximation for the actual coupling functions. This approach has the advantage of permitting analysis to proceed without having to introduce spacing and thickness as qualifiers at each step. Further, by using y' the results can be applied to both contact ($\delta \approx 0$) and non-contact recording, with no need to uniquely distinguish between them. In practice, d is usually less than or of the same order of magnitude as γ and δ, and hence $\mathbf{H}(x, y')$ will represent a very good approximation for the coupling field, from which the actual writing and reading behavior of the magnetic recording configuration can be predicted.

Idealized Ring Head

The objectives in head design for both the functions of reading and writing are compatible with respect to the importance of a high field gradient for the fringing flux. For writing, we desire a sharp magnetizing field to as closely as possible achieve step-function changes in magnetization. To saturate the recording medium on writing, it is also necessary however to obtain an intense magnetizing field at the surface. The only head design variable available with an idealized ring head is the gap γ and our only control over the fringing field is through selection of this parameter. We will investigate here the influence of the head gap on the writing and reading performance of the idealized magnetic head.

Writing—Gap Size. The maximum value of the fringing (or magnetizing) field exists along the head gap centerline. It was shown in Chapter 4 that the field $H_x(0, y')$ can be closely approximated by the following expression:

$$H_x(0, y') = \frac{2H_g}{\pi} \left[\tan^{-1} \frac{\gamma}{2y'} \right] \qquad (5.3)$$

For $y' = \gamma/2$, the maximum fringing field is 50% of the gap field. Figure 5.2 is a curve of the ratio of the fringing field $H_x(0, y')$ to the internal gap field as a function of y'/γ.

The rapid attenuation of the fringing field with increasing distance from the head is apparent. For this reason, a ratio of y'/γ less than 2.0 is generally necessary to adequately couple the magnetic head to the surface for writing. Since in practice, the minimum value of y' is often fixed by spacing and surface layer requirements, this factor may also be regarded as actually establishing a lower limit for the size of the writing

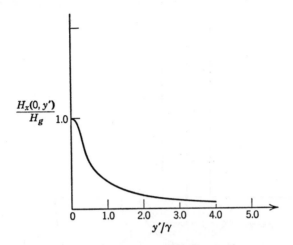

Fig. 5.2. Attenuation of gap fringing field.

gap. If a single head element is used for both writing and reading, this restriction may call for design compromises in the magnetic head in order that it may serve properly both recording functions.

Reading—The Magnetic Coupling Function. We are particularly interested in the *spread* of the fringing field along the x axis, since this factor sets the actual bit resolution of the recording system in reading. This fringing field distribution is of particular interest in digital magnetic recording, for it directly determines the pulse width and shape obtained from discontinuous changes in magnetization.

In longitudinal recording, the surface magnetization is primarily horizontal. For this reason the fringing field component of principal interest is H_x. Although considering only H_x will, in general, provide adequate performance predictability, we shall also examine the nature of H_y. The inclusion of H_y in the analysis will provide a means to determine what degree of vertical magnetization can be tolerated before the output signal width is adversely affected. Further, an understanding of the nature of H_y will reveal the type of signal perturbation or distortion that would arise from a small component of vertical magnetization.

For purposes of discussion we divide the gap fringing field region into two zones: $y' \geq \gamma$ and $y' < \gamma$. This division has been made because very near the gap the fringing field is not amenable to simple analytical formulation, this region being indicated in Fig. 5.3 by the shaded area. However, for $y' \geq \gamma$ we can approximate the fringing field closely with a simple analytical expression (the accuracy improving with increasing y').

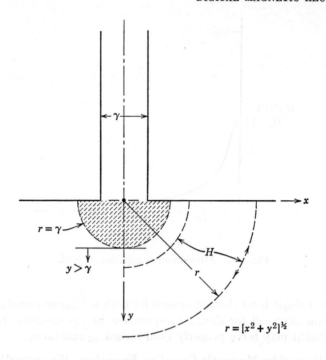

Fig. 5.3. Fringing field zones: Idealized ring head.

In the range $y' < \gamma$, reasonable qualitative estimations of the fringing field vector components can be established for illustrative purposes. Thus it will be possible in a straightforward manner to provide an insight into the overall nature of the fringing field and consequently the character of the pulse output when operating under diverse conditions.

(a) $y' \geq \gamma$

For the case $y' \geq \gamma$ we can approximate the fringing field by a semi-circular field distribution (see Fig. 5.3). Thus,

$$|H| \propto \frac{1}{r} \qquad (5.4)$$

where r is the distance from the gap centerline intersection with the pole face plane to the point in question. Then, from Chapter 4,

$$\frac{H_x(x, y')}{H_x(0, y')} = \frac{1}{1 + (x/y')^2} \qquad (5.5)$$

Now

$$H_y = |H| \cdot \left(\frac{x}{r}\right) = H_x(0, y')y' \frac{x}{r^2} \tag{5.6}$$

or

$$\frac{H_y(x, y')}{H_x(0, y')} = \frac{x/y'}{1 + (x/y')^2} \tag{5.7}$$

We can calculate the points where H_y is a maxima or minima by taking the derivative of the right side of equation (5.7) with respect to x and setting it equal to zero. Doing this we get a maximum at $x = y'$ and a minimum at $x = -y'$. Substituting these values of x into equation (5.7) gives a value of $\pm \frac{1}{2}$ for the ratio of $H_y|_{\max}$ to $H_x|_{\max}$.

In Fig. 5.4 are plotted the curves of H_x and H_y as given by equations (5.5) and (5.7). Their amplitudes are normalized by the factor $H_x(0, y')$, and the distance measure is u (where $u = x/y'$). In this form these two curves are a dimensionless representation of the fringing field for $y' \geq \gamma$ and as such are applicable for any selected value of y' in this range. This one set of curves then serves for the whole fringing field zone.

If we define the spread Δx of the horizontal fringing field between its 10% relative amplitude points by η, then $\eta/y' = 6$. Thus, for a step change in horizontal magnetization, the resulting output voltage pulse will have a pulse width (measured between its 10% amplitude points)

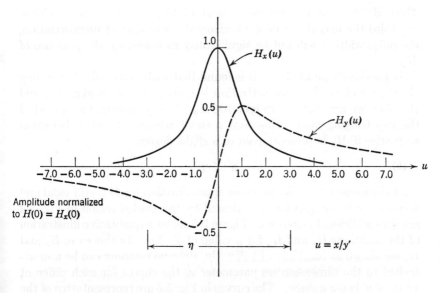

Fig. 5.4. Fringing field components H_x and H_y ($y' \geq \gamma$).

equal to approximately six times the separation between the magnetic head and the midplane of the recording surface. This distance measure of pulse width is converted into time by dividing by the surface velocity v.

The $H_y(u)$ curve of Fig. 5.4 shows the nature of the readback signal component for a recorded step change in vertical magnetization. The deleterious influence of a significant vertical magnetization component upon bit resolution is readily apparent from the slow drop-off of H_y with increasing u. Further, the presence of appreciable vertical magnetization would make in a step magnetization change the output pulse highly asymmetric, since the total signal is obtained by adding the two waveform components shown, with the relative amplitudes corresponding to their respective intensities of surface magnetization.

To determine a bound on the ratio of vertical to horizontal recorded magnetization tolerable before a noticeable decrease in the pulse resolution would occur we can require

$$M_y H_y(u = 3) \leq 0.1$$

where

$$M_x H_x(0) \equiv 1.0$$

This condition (corresponding to the method just given of measuring pulse width) gives

$$M_y \leq 0.1/0.3 = .33$$

Thus, if M_y (the vertical component of magnetization) is less than one-third the magnitude of the horizontal component of magnetization, the pulse width η will not be significantly increased by the presence of M_y.

As previously pointed out, it is found that with longitudinal recording the degree of vertical magnetization is quite small (or negligible), and therefore we are justified in ignoring H_y when estimating the spread of the gap fringing field. However, a small amount of signal distortion may arise if M_y is present, even to a slight degree.

(b) $y' < \gamma$

At distances $r > \gamma$ the previous approximation for $\mathbf{H}$ is still valid and therefore only the gap locale indicated by the shaded region in Fig. 5.3 requires additional attention. Figure 5.5 shows a qualitative illustration of the functions H_x and H_y for a value of $y' < \gamma$. In this case, H_x and H_y are shown as functions of x directly, since no meaning can be now attached to the dimensionless parameter u, the curves for each different value of y' being unique. The curves in Fig. 5.5 are representative of the general nature of the magnetic field functions in this zone, however.

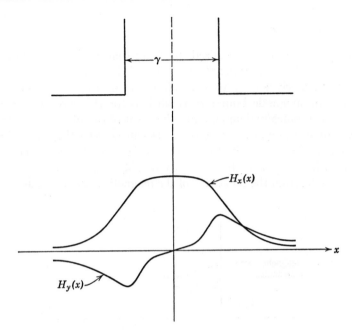

Fig. 5.5. Fringing field components H_x and H_y ($y' \ll \gamma$).

It can be seen in this instance that the gap size is the predominant spatial parameter setting the *shape* of the fringing field. H_x is the key function for longitudinal recording, and under the condition $y'/\gamma \rightarrow 0$ the gap primarily determines the recording resolution. Hence a reduction in gap size gives an almost proportional reduction in pulse width for a step change in horizontal magnetization.

The fringing field function H_x becomes progressively more "bell-shaped" as y' is reduced and approaches and then becomes less than γ. Thus, H_x can frequently be suitably approximated by a Gaussian curve for any chosen value of y'. This is particularly valuable when studying signal-recording techniques because of the suitability of the normal distribution function to mathematical analysis.

For high-density recording, the parameters γ, δ, and d all tend to be in the range of tens to hundreds of microinches. The actual values will depend on the state of that technology which tends to first limit the minimum value that can be chosen for one of these parameters, this parameter in turn setting the framework for optimization. Thus, the gap dimension is a head fabrication problem, the recording medium thickness a magnetic coating or plating problem, and the head spacing a mechanics problem.

Pole Tip Contour

A modification to the idealized ring head that can often result in improved resolution is to taper the pole tips of the magnetic head, a technique particularly suited to non-contact recording. This procedure modifies the magnetic boundary conditions for the gap fringing field. Figure 5.6 graphically demonstrates the effect of this change in pole face contour upon the gap fringing field. It can be seen that the effect of narrow pole tips is to shift the effective origin for the "far zone" magnetic field forward of the head face by roughly a distance $y = \Delta$. This change results from the relocation of the magnetic equipotentials respon-

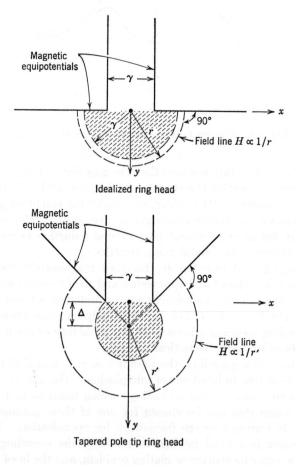

Fig. 5.6.   Effect of tapered pole tips.

sible for the head fringing field (recall that a field line must be perpendicular to an equipotential line).

For a value of y' well outside the "near zone" field region, the shaded area in Fig. 5.6, we can still use the H_x curve of Fig. 5.4 to determine the spread of the field. However, we must replace y' by $(y' - \Delta)$, since the effective origin of this fringing field has been displaced by Δ in the positive y direction. (Note from the figure that y' in this instance must always be greater than 2Δ.)

Thus the pulse width η will be approximately equal to $6(y' - \Delta)$.

For the design shown in Fig. 5.6, $\Delta = \gamma/2$. Consider, for example, $y' = 1.5\gamma$. Then, for perfectly flat pole faces

$$\eta \approx 9\gamma$$

while here

$$\eta \approx 6(1.5\gamma - 0.5\gamma) = 6\gamma$$

Thus in this instance a 50% reduction in pulse width is realizable by tapering the pole faces of the magnetic head. This percentage improvement has actually been achieved in practice through this head design technique (7). It can be recognized that the potential gain in resolution applies when y' is outside the near-gap region. For this reason this particular technique of head design has evolved and only been applied for non-contact recording, where the prerequisite conditions can arise.

This magnetic head contouring reduces also the spread of the magnetizing field for writing. The magnetizing field magnitude at distance y' will be reduced compared to an idealized ring head, however, since the line integral of H along a field line (here also a line of constant field intensity) traverses a relatively longer path between the two pole faces. Thus, for the same writing current $H_x(0, y')$ is less. Care must be taken therefore to ascertain that the writing field is still able to saturate the recording surface. The angle of taper along with the gap dimension sets the value of Δ. It must be possible to make Δ large enough to realize a significant improvement to make the special fabrication effort and the likely additional cost of this type of head worthwhile.

Reading Coil Location

Figure 5.7 shows the magnetic potential lines for an entire head structure so that the influence of the reading coil location will become evident. The magnetic potential lines shown are not actually meaningful within the coil (being a current source region). However, the size and location of the coil on the magnetic core does reflect in the gross magnetic field

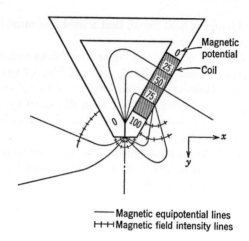

Fig. 5.7. Influence of read coil location on magnetic coupling field.

distribution of a magnetic head. Usually the coil location is not important to pulse shape, since it does not affect the effective gap-fringing field. In some magnetic head configurations (such as the one shown in Fig. 5.7) however, the position of the coil, through its non-symmetrical location on the head core, can unbalance the readback pulse "tails" through its modification of the head-surface coupling function outside the immediate gap area. The head structure illustrated reveals the unbalance that can arise in the flux along a plane in front of the head gap from placing the coil on only one leg. In sine wave recording, the location of the coil on the magnetic head core would manifest itself only in the very long wavelength response, that is, where the wavelengths become of the same order as the physical size of the head itself.

To estimate the fringing field outside the immediate gap area, it is advisable to make a coarse field map which encompasses the entire head geometry, including the actual location and distribution of the read coil windings on the core. This type of magnetic field map is easily constructed by substituting for the coil a magnetic potential source gradient as shown in Fig. 5.7. Further, this type of mapping will indicate the non-useful leakage flux associated with the magnetic head, which is usually considerable.

Magnetic Circuit of the Magnetic Head

Figure 5.8 shows a typical magnetic recording head-recording surface combination with an equivalent electrical circuit analog after Kornei (5).

R_c is the reluctance of one leg.

R_l is the leakage reluctance at the inner edge of the front gap.

R_g is the front gap reluctance.

R_b is the reluctance of the back gap (note the head has a back gap because of the method of construction).

R_d is the reluctance of the path between one pole and the recording medium.

R_s is the reluctance of the recording medium across the gap between the poles.

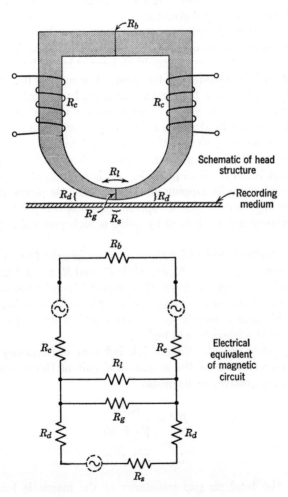

Fig. 5.8. Equivalent magnetic circuit of a magnetic head.

This electrical circuit analog serves to determine and focus attention on the key flux paths. Magnetic reluctance is nominally proportional to the following parameters; that is,

$$R \propto \frac{l}{\mu A} \qquad (5.8)$$

where l = path length,
$\quad A$ = cross-sectional area of path, and
$\quad \mu$ = relative permeability.

These variables then provide means of having some control over the division of flux in the head structure.

In the equivalent electric circuit, for writing, voltage sources would exist in the branches containing R_c (the legs of the magnetic head), while for reading, the voltage source would be located in the branch with R_s.

R_d and R_s are independent of the head. For reading it is desirable to increase R_g and R_l, since these reluctances tend to shunt the flux away from the magnetic core path. This normally means that the cross-sectional area of the front gap is reduced by providing a very small gap height (of the order of 10 to 100 times γ) and bringing the pole pieces together at as wide an internal angle as practical. All the other reluctances should be as small as possible. R_b is minimized by providing a large area and carefully lapping and fitting the pole pieces at the back to minimize any "non-magnetic" spacing effect at this joint. The other head reluctances are minimized by using a high permeability material for the core.

The same basic objectives for these reluctances exist from a consideration of the writing process. Again, while R_d and R_s are not uniquely associated with the head, the lower these equivalent reluctances the more efficiently the head and surface are magnetically coupled together. Normally this goal is merely synonymous with a desire to reduce the dimensions of the fringing field region.

We have yet to consider the possible influence of frequency ($f = v/\lambda$) in the characterization of the magnetic circuit of the magnetic head. Towards this objective, let us define

$$R_g' = \frac{R_g R_l}{R_g + R_l}$$

and

$$R_a = R_g' + R_b$$

R_a is then the total air gap reluctance of the magnetic head circuit, produced by non-magnetic sections in the magnetic head flux path.

Further, let
$$R_m = 2R_c$$

That is, R_m is that part of the magnetic head reluctance associated with the magnetic core. Thus,

$$R_h = R_a + R_m$$

where R_h is the total reluctance of the magnetic circuit of the magnetic head.

On readback, the surface magnetization gives rise to a flux ϕ_t, which divides between the magnetic core path and the front gap path of the magnetic head in inverse relation to the reluctances of these two paths. If we define ϕ_m as the flux through the magnetic head core, then

$$\frac{\phi_m}{\phi_t} = \frac{R_g'}{R_h} \tag{5.9}$$

Now the "air gap" reluctance term R_g' is not frequency (time) dependent but the reluctance of the magnetic core R_m will be, because of the eddy current and hysteresis energy losses in the magnetic material comprising the core of the magnetic head. We will indicate the functional dependence of R_m on frequency by $R_m(f)$. As a consequence, R_h will also be written as $R_h(f)$ in the discussions to follow.

We can now define a frequency sensitivity factor $S(f)$ for a magnetic head in the following manner:

$$S(f) = \frac{R_h(0)}{R_h(f)} = \frac{1 + \dfrac{R_m(0)}{R_a}}{1 + \dfrac{R_m(f)}{R_a}} \tag{5.10}$$

$S(f)$ is the ratio of flux through the magnetic head core at a given frequency f to the value at $f = 0$. Now,

$$S(f) < 1.0$$

since as we saw in Chapter 3 both eddy current and hysteresis losses increase with frequency. Further, the output voltage

$$e(f) \propto fS(f) \tag{5.11}$$

where again, $f = v/\lambda$, with λ being the recorded wavelength. Recall that the output voltage is proportional to the derivative of the magnetic head flux and therefore, for a lossless magnetic head core, the output voltage is directly proportional to frequency. If $R_m(f) < R_a$ in the frequency range of interest, that is, the reluctance of the core is always small compared with that of the gap(s), then $S(f) \approx 1.0$ and $e(f)$ is proportional to f.

On writing, the magnetizing field at the recording surface is proportional to the flux setup in the magnetic head by the current in the write coil. Thus

$$\phi_h(f) = \frac{\text{mmf}}{R_h(f)} \qquad (5.12)$$

The writing efficiency of a magnetic head is inversely proportional to $R_h(f)$. Therefore, the same frequency sensitivity ratio is applicable to writing as well as to reading; $S(f)$ gives the factor by which the writing mmf must be increased with frequency in order to maintain a constant magnetizing field intensity.

When the cross-sectional area of the magnetic head flux path is relatively uniform

$$\frac{R_m(0)}{R_a} \approx \frac{1}{\mu} \left[\frac{\text{magnetic path length}}{\text{non-magnetic path length}} \right] \qquad (5.13)$$

where μ is the relative permeability of the magnetic head core compared to air.

The effect of magnetic core losses on the frequency response can be minimized, other than through selection of the magnetic material, by (a) making the head gap γ as large as possible, compatible with the pulse resolution requirements; (b) introducing an appreciable gap at the rear of the head if the absolute head sensitivity permits—normally not possible with read heads since signal output is usually of overriding importance; and (c) making the magnetic core path as short as feasible. For a magnetic head specialized for writing a loss of absolute sensitivity can be offset by increasing the write current amplitude.

ELECTRICAL CHARACTERISTICS OF MAGNETIC HEADS

When we speak of the electrical characteristics of magnetic heads, we are essentially referring to the frequency behavior of the magnetic head transducer and the manner in which it influences design and performance. The frequency aspects of the magnetic head are only a function of the time domain and therefore can be unified with the spatial wavelength behavior, in the context of presenting the overall recording process performance, only in terms of a specific surface velocity as it is required that f be related to λ through the expression $f = v/\lambda$.

Basically two types of magnetic materials, ferrites and metallic laminations, are available for magnetic head construction. Both the magnetic and electrical properties of these two categories of materials differ widely. In addition to the influence that eddy current and hysteresis losses have on the frequency response of a magnetic head, we must give attention to the fact that these energy losses may give rise to a measurable thermal heating of the magnetic core. Therefore, each of these two types of core materials will be discussed individually in terms of the nature of the influence its class of properties has on the electrical behavior of the magnetic head.

Ferrite Cores

The resistivity of a conventional ferrite material is a million or more times that of the common metallic magnetic alloys, and eddy current losses are negligible. In general, the permeabilities and maximum flux densities are much lower, and the coercivities are much higher, than those of metallic magnetic materials. The main disadvantage of ferrites with respect to magnetic heads, however, is the difficulty of fabricating out of this brittle ceramic material, precisely dimensioned head gaps whose edges will not chip, etc., under prolonged abrasion and impact.

The power loss in a ferrite head arises from hysteresis, and this fact is important when writing, since at this time a high flux density is required (in order to magnetize the recording surface), and more particularly when writing at high pulse rates. As demonstrated in Chapter 3,

$$P_h \propto f \int H \, dB \qquad (5.14)$$

where P_h is the hysteresis power loss and the integral represents the area of the B-H loop traversed during each frequency cycle. The presence of this latter term makes evident the reason writing is of concern. A ferrite material with a low coercivity is highly desirable.

Attention must also be given to the possibly appreciable heating of the magnetic head core produced by hysteresis effects on writing. Special design precautions may be necessary to assure that the thermal energy generated is effectively conducted away, recognizing the insulator qualities of ferrite. Elevated temperatures of the ferrite core may not only damage the coil-winding insulation and perhaps the recording surface and its free movement but can also reduce the ferromagnetic properties of the magnetic head core to a marked degree, even to the point of rendering it completely ineffectual if the Curie temperature of the material is approached.

Laminated Heads

The most frequently used magnetic material for magnetic head cores are nickel-iron alloys, used in laminated stacks. These magnetic substances have extremely high permeabilities and comparatively low resistivities (or high conductivities), and they are used in the form of thin sheets or laminations to minimize eddy current losses. Usually, with metallic magnetic materials the eddy current loss will be much greater than the associated hysteresis loss, even for the operation of writing. This results in part from the redistribution of flux in the core produced by the eddy currents.

As we have seen, the magnetic head can be viewed as a one-dimensional magnetic circuit. Then, to derive the frequency characteristic of the magnetic head caused by induced eddy currents, we will solve

$$\frac{d^2B}{dx^2} = j\omega\mu_0\mu\sigma B \qquad (5.15)$$

subject to the boundary conditions imposed by the choice of lamination thickness, g. This equation, developed in Chapter 3, gives the space-time behavior of the magnetic flux density in a conductor material for a time periodic field of angular frequency ω ($\omega = 2\pi f$). Since, per lamination,

$$\phi_m = \int_{-g/2}^{g/2} B \, dg \qquad (5.16)$$

by solving equation (5.15), substituting the result into equation (5.16), and carrying out the indicated integration we obtain, where

$$\phi_m = |\phi_m| \, \underline{/\theta}$$

that

$$\left|\frac{\phi_m(f)}{\phi_m(0)}\right| = \frac{1}{\sqrt{2}a} \left[\frac{\sinh^2 a + \sin^2 a}{\sinh^2 a + \cos^2 a}\right]^{1/2} \qquad (5.17)$$

and

$$\theta(f) = \tan^{-1}\left[\frac{\sin 2a}{\sinh 2a}\right] - \frac{\pi}{4} \qquad (5.18)$$

where

$$a = \frac{g}{2}\sqrt{\pi\mu_0\mu\sigma f} \qquad (5.19)$$

We note that $\theta(0) = 0$.

The term $1/\sqrt{\pi\mu_0\mu\sigma f}$ has the dimensions of distance and is familiarly known as the depth of penetration or skin depth in describing the skin effect in current carrying conductors. For a semi-infinite block the depth of penetration is the depth (from the outer surface where the source field is applied) at which the field intensity B would decay to $1/e$ (or 36.7%) of its value at the surface.

For frequencies at which a is greater than 5 (or the skin depth is approximately one tenth of the lamination thickness) we have, from equations (5.17) and (5.18),

$$\frac{\phi_m(f)}{\phi_m(0)} = \frac{1}{\sqrt{2}a} \underline{/-45°}$$

As we have already seen

$$R_m(f) \propto \frac{1}{\phi_m(f)}$$

and therefore

$$R_m(f) = \sqrt{2}aR_m(0)\underline{/45°} \tag{5.20}$$

in this frequency range. We note that because of eddy currents the reluctance of the magnetic head core becomes complex and introduces a phase lag in the head flux approaching as a limit 45°. For these frequencies, almost all the magnetic head flux (on both reading and writing) is carried by the surface layers of the laminations. Even so, if

$$R_m(f) < R_a$$

in this frequency range, the head sensitivity will not be significantly reduced. At these higher frequencies, when

$$R_m(f) > R_a$$

then

$$S(f) \propto 1/a \tag{5.21}$$

and thus

$$e(f) \propto fS(f) \propto f^{1/2} \tag{5.22}$$

Expression (5.22) then indicates the manner in which the output voltage eventually varies with frequency (in time) as the frequency increases.

Since

$$a \propto gf^{1/2}$$

to extend the frequency response of a magnetic head by a factor of 45, the thickness of the laminations used should be reduced by a factor of 2.

Equivalent Lumped-Constant Electrical Circuit of the Magnetic Head

The output voltage on reading and the magnetizing force on writing are both proportional to the number of turns on the read/write coil(s).

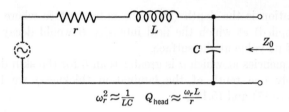

$$\omega_r^2 \approx \frac{1}{LC} \quad Q_{head} \approx \frac{\omega_r L}{r}$$

Fig. 5.9. Simplified equivalent electrical circuit of magnetic head.

These facts indicate that it should be advantageous to make the number of turns N as large as practical. The inductance of the magnetic head is proportional to N^2, however. Furthermore, the coil winding capacity increases with N. Therefore the larger the value for N, the lower the resonant frequency of the magnetic head and the greater the time constants associated with its transient electrical response.

The lumped-constant circuit shown in Fig. 5.9 will normally suffice to represent the equivalent electrical circuit of the magnetic head for the electrical design aspects of the digital magnetic recording system. In Fig. 5.9, C is the effective shunt capacity associated with the magnetic head and includes not only the contribution from the head coil but also the lead capacity between the head and the first stage of electronics. Both the resistance r and the inductance L will actually be functions of frequency whenever it is necessary to account for the frequency loss function of the magnetic head core in the circuit design.

Usually the Q of a magnetic head is quite low (less than 10). The inductance L is relatively low compared to its associated coil resistance because of the inherent air gap(s) in the magnetic circuit of a magnetic head (recall that $L \propto 1/R_h$). Thus, a magnetic head typically has a broad frequency resonance peak. For pulse recording one customarily operates below ω_r, that is, where the head impedance is still inductive in character. This procedure minimizes spurious output signal oscillations on readback.

In high-frequency digital magnetic recording heads the effective output impedance of the head (called Z_0 in Fig. 5.9) may be only of the order of one hundred to several hundred ohms. Normally then, during readback the head is terminated with a relatively low impedance, for example, of one thousand ohms. This is done to provide some damping, in order to reduce or eliminate any pulse overshoots (or ringing) i.e., waveform distortion associated with the electrical characteristics of the magnetic head.

Cross-Talk and Interhead Shielding

Cross-talk refers to the magnetic coupling between magnetic heads mounted in close proximity, and it is of concern when the heads must be simultaneously operated. The most obvious example is recording in parallel on a group of tracks with a set of magnetic heads arrayed in a common mounting block.

For high frequencies effective shielding can be achieved through enclosing or separating the head from its environment by a shield of a high-conductivity material such as copper. The screening action results from the induced eddy currents in this conductor surface. Here, we deliberately seek an eddy current effect, and the thickness of the shield should be several times the depth of penetration for the frequency range for which the shield is to serve, if it is to be fully effective.

For low frequencies, the most effective magnetic shielding approach is to insert two or three high permeability magnetic screens, with intervening spacers, between heads to act as shunts for the flux tending to spread from one magnetic head to the other. It can be proved that several such magnetic shields, separated from each other by non-magnetic layers, are much more effective than one single shield of equivalent net thickness.

Thus, in general, one will find that where excellent magnetic shielding between heads is required, a sandwich design composed of alternate layers of copper and some high-permeability magnetic medium is inserted between the groups of magnetic head laminations in the head stack.

HEAD-TRACK REGISTRATION

In digital magnetic recording the importance of high storage density places emphasis on track density as well as bit density. The surface area information density in bits per square inch is equal to the product of track density times bit density. Head-to-surface track registration tolerances are necessary in any mechanical structure designed to produce some required relative motion between a transducer and storage medium. With a single read/write head element it is necessary, in order to accommodate this lack of precise registration, to accept in readback a "noise" component, arising from residual patterns at the track edges from previous recordings. A track must then be wide enough (at the price of track density) to overcome this and yield a suitable signal-to-noise ratio. A dual-element head unit is a special means to compensate for significant lateral track misalignment.

A common form of dual-element head structure is an erase-wide

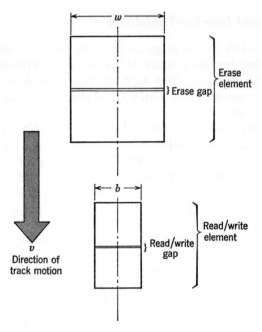

Fig. 5.10.   Erase-wide read/write-narrow head.

read/write-narrow device, shown schematically in Fig. 5.10.   In this
unit the individual elements are aligned along a centerline and placed so
that the erase element precedes the read/write element with respect to
the direction of track motion.   The advantage to be gained by this head
arrangement can be seen by reference to Fig. 5.11.

Here let

$$\pm P = \text{head-to-medium lateral registration tolerance}$$
and
$$b = \text{read/write head width}$$
$$w = \text{erase head width}$$

On each writing operation the erase head is energized to eradicate all
previously recorded information across its width w.   This means that

$$w - 2P$$

is the guaranteed width of the erased band under any combination of
circumstances.   Furthermore,

$$b + 2P$$

is the width of the band within which the read/write track must occur.

By requiring the following inequality,

$$b + 2P \leq w - 2P \tag{5.23}$$

the read/write element is constrained to fall always within the erased zone. This relation gives

$$w \geq b + 4P \tag{5.24}$$

as a restriction on the minimum width of the erase element relative to the read/write head width b.

Writing is a separate operation from reading, therefore these operations take place on different passages of the track by the head. In order

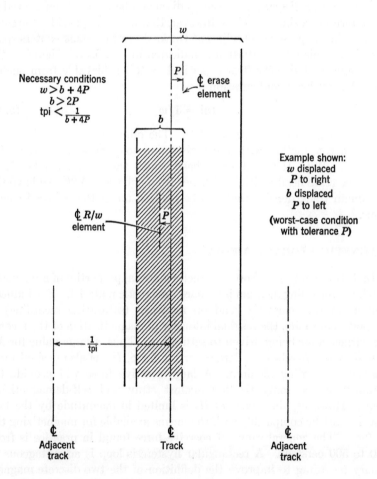

Fig. 5.11. Track registration, erase-wide read/write-narrow head unit.

to be sure that the read pass always senses at least a portion of the most recently recorded signal, the following condition must also be met:

$$b - 2P > 0 \qquad (5.25)$$

The larger the ratio b/P, the more constant will be the reading signal for a given lateral registration tolerance.   This dual-element type of head unit assures that no output signal "noise" will arise from the anticipated variations in lateral track registration.   A good signal-to-noise ratio, comparable to that obtainable from perfect track alignment, then can be expected if the basic signal-to-noise ratio of the recording system is high to begin with.

The lateral registration tolerances discussed here have been viewed so far in terms of a single track.   However, this approach provides the same features in the presence of adjacent tracks down to a track centers spacing of w.   This latter situation is indicated in Fig. 5.11.   Therefore the maximum track density (tracks per inch = tpi) achievable from such a dual-element head configuration is

$$\text{tpi} = 1/w \qquad (5.26)$$

where w is given by equation (5.24).   The minimum acceptable signal, taken in conjunction with the registration tolerances required ($\pm P$), set b_{min}.   With the read/write head width thus set, formula (5.24) gives the erase head width, and hence from equation (5.26) we have the maximum track density that can be realized under the imposed conditions.

MAGNETIC STORAGE MEDIA

In distinction to the "soft" magnetic material properties of a magnetic head, the recording medium is a "hard" magnetic material.   The induced voltage in the magnetic head on readback (saturation recording) is proportional to M_r, the residual intensity of magnetization of the recording surface after being driven to saturation.   Thus, a large value for M_r is indicated.   A relatively large coercive force, H_c, is also desired for a magnetic recording medium.   A large coercive force will provide for stability of the magnetization against stray and self-demagnetizing fields.   However, the choice of H_c is limited in magnitude by the fact that it must be compatible with the means available for magnetizing the surface.   The general range of coercive force found in practice is from 200 to 500 oersteds.   A rectangular hysteresis loop is advantageous in binary recording to improve the definition of the two discrete magnetization states used.   Rather than permeability, the ratio M_r/M_s is more meaningful (the "squareness ratio" used for magnetic memory cores).

The magnetic switching characteristics of recording media must be extremely fast, so that time-dependent effects do not limit the recording performance. In digital magnetic recording, current rise (or fall) times of less than 0.1 microsecond at current switching repetition rates of greater than a megacycle are commonly used. At these speeds, both magnetic oxide and plated surfaces can respond with no apparent time delay.

Magnetic Recording Surfaces

Magnetic recording media occur in the form of magnetic oxide coatings and metallic magnetic films.

Magnetic oxide surfaces are composed of iron oxide particles dispersed in a suitable binder. The oxides used are the synthetic iron oxide, γ-Fe_2O_3 (red) or magnetite, Fe_3O_4 (black). The red iron oxide is by far the most commonly employed. This magnetic oxide is available in suspensions with an average particle size less than one micron in diameter. Typical magnetic characteristics are: $H_c = 250$ oersteds, $B_r = 500$ gauss.

The synthetic iron oxide has proved to be the most satisfactory recording medium to date. Extremely homogeneous and uniform coatings have been achieved. Further, the method of application tends to "fill" and mask minor surface irregularities in the substrate. While a typical magnetic oxide surface is about one-thousandth of an inch thick, magnetic oxide recording films slightly thinner than 100 microinches have been commercially developed.

Metallic magnetic surfaces have long been used for digital magnetic recording and there has been a renewed interest in the potential of cobalt-nickel platings for recording at densities in excess of 1000 bits per inch. Plating techniques are inherently suited to the production of very thin films. Therefore, with technology progressing in all facets of the magnetic recording art, it is natural that metallic films would again draw major attention. For conventional cobalt-nickel platings, H_c is approximately 200 oersteds and B_r in the neighborhood of 10,000 gauss. Co-Ni films, in contrast to magnetic oxide coatings, permit a wide range of B-H relationships to be realized. Co-Ni magnetic recording surfaces have been produced successfully down to a thickness in the range of 10 microinches.

The major direction of development efforts in magnetic recording media is to achieve ever thinner magnetic recording surfaces. The potential gain in pulse resolution from a decrease in recording surface thickness, through a reduction in the magnetic coupling distance along a track between head and surface, has been described previously. The related bit density increase offered by going to thinner magnetic films usually more than justifies the loss in readback signal amplitude that results.

Necessarily, higher bit densities require higher-quality recording surfaces and therefore further advances in surface quality must be sought along with technical progress in producing thinner magnetic recording layers.

The emphasis of this book is on the principles of digital magnetic recording and therefore will not go into the subject of recording media technology. Rather, we shall focus on the relation between the magnetic properties of recording media and their specific influence on the storage of digital (or binary) information in magnetic recording films.

It has been found in practice that for equivalent pulse resolution a cobalt-nickel plating must be several times thinner than an iron oxide coating. This variance in performance appears due to their differing magnetic rather than electrical properties. The hypothesis advanced here and developed in the next section, in terms of discrete state magnetic recording, attributes this difference in behavior to self-demagnetization within the magnetic surface. The necessity to go to thinner cobalt-nickel platings, to achieve with them resolutions comparable to magnetic oxide coatings, also means that the much larger signal amplitudes one might hope to obtain with such platings (having a much larger B_r than iron oxide) cannot actually be realized. Even so, plated films still appear to offer the greater ultimate bit-storage density.

The results of the analysis to follow support the point of view that self-demagnetization has not been a major factor in digital magnetic recording. A recording surface could be readily produced in a sufficiently thin layer to nullify the influence of self-demagnetization, yet still be one limiting factor on resolution through film thickness alone. With continuing progress in technology this situation may be expected to change and place greater emphasis on achieving specific magnetic properties for magnetic recording media to secure further advances in digital storage density; whereas recording performance, even at 1000 bits per inch, is relatively insensitive to significant differences in the B-H characteristic of magnetic recording surfaces.

Self-Demagnetization

After the writing and passage of newly recorded information from the magnetic head, this recorded magnetization will give rise to a self-demagnetizing field within the storage medium. During the time a recorded region traverses by the magnetic head, its demagnetizing field is decreased considerably by the presence of the head, this effect being similar to that obtaining from the use of a keeper on a permanent magnet. Since the recorded magnetization does not decrease noticeably with repeated scanning, no appreciable irreversible changes result from this action, and an equilibrium situation can therefore be considered to exist in the recording medium.

In digital magnetic recording we deal only with discrete changes in magnetization. Therefore our principal concern, with respect to self-demagnetization, is the influence this phenomenon has on the transition width of a magnetization change. The preceding discussion of the writing process (Chapter 4) gave an estimate for x_1, the recorded width of a change in the direction of saturation. In our consideration of self-demagnetization, we will look at the minimum supportable transition width in the surface from the point of view of the magnetic properties of the recording medium itself. One would expect the larger of these two values for x_1, arising from two different phenomena, to set the actual bit-storage limit of the surface. (Irrespective of the dominant mechanism, as stated earlier the basic recording resolution has been principally set by the reading process.)

Figure 5.12 illustrates the M-H characteristic of a recording medium in the third quadrant (the demagnetization curve). The *self*-demagnetizing field acting on a differential volume of the medium may be expressed

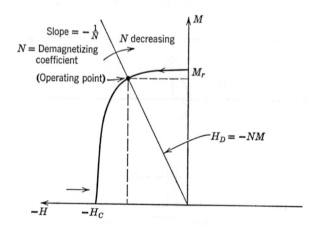

Fig. 5.12. Self-demagnetization.

as follows:
$$H_D = -NM \tag{5.27}$$

where H_D = the self-demagnetizing field
      N = the demagnetizing coefficient, which is a function of the magnetic geometry of the region (here N is always positive) and
      M = the existing intensity of magnetization

Now the actual equilibrium state of a magnetic region is given by the simultaneous solution of equation (5.27) and the given M-H functional relation of the recording medium. A solution is readily obtained when these two relations are expressed as curves (normally the M-H property of the material is always given graphically), through a determination of their point of intersection.

We are interested specifically in the demagnetization that can be supported by a unit volume of the magnetic material without causing an appreciable reduction in its magnetization, when it is assumed to have been saturated. This state point is indicated on Fig. 5.12.

To develop a mathematical model, let us start by considering a surface when an ideal step change in saturation magnetization is hypothesized. The track width is assumed to be infinite, since it is so large compared to the other dimensions involved. Now refer to Fig. 5.13. We shall ignore the associated south poles, since their location is normally sufficiently remote that they could not significantly modify H_D. All vectors can be treated as if they were scalar quantities, since uniaxial magnetization is necessarily implied here.

Now,
$$B = \mu_0[H + M] \tag{5.28}$$

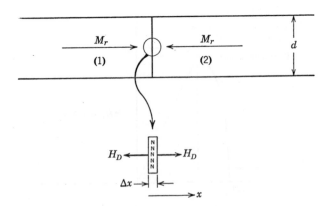

Fig. 5.13. Step change in saturation magnetization.

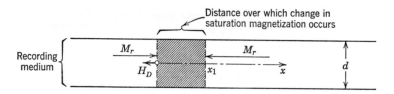

Fig. 5.14. Finite saturation magnetization reversal.

We have at the boundary of the magnetization change

$$H_2 - H_1 = -(M_2 - M_1) \tag{5.29}$$

since

$$\nabla \cdot \mathbf{B} = 0 \qquad \text{and thus} \qquad B_2 = B_1$$

Then, substituting in equation (5.29) the values given in Fig. 5.13, we have

$$H_D = -M_r \tag{5.30}$$

that is, $N = 1.0$, since this result does not depend on a particular value of M. The normal recording medium could not support a perfect step change in magnetization. For an iron oxide layer with $B_r = 500$ gauss and $H_c = 250$ oersteds, N should not exceed approximately $\frac{1}{2}$ if such a step discontinuity in M_r is to be sustained (recall that $M_r = B_r$). The situation is even more unfavorable with a material like cobalt-nickel.

Now look at the "pillbox," shown in Fig. 5.13, enclosing the magnetic transition (step). The flux per unit surface area normal to the x axis, flowing out of this enclosing surface (in the limit as $\Delta x \to 0$) is equal to $2[\mu_0 M_r]$. The equivalent magnetic charge density on this boundary is then equal to $2M_r$ (Chapter 3).

Figure 5.14 presents a model for a finite reversal in saturation magnetization. The distance between the two opposite directions of saturation is x_1. The net magnetic charge between these two boundaries is $2M_r$, the same as it is for the step change, since the number of uncompensated magnetic poles in this region is fixed. We assume here that the magnetic charge is uniformly distributed. Intuitively we expect that H_D (acting to demagnetize the medium at the plane $x = 0$ where $M = M_r$) will be progressively reduced as the distance x_1 is increased. The minimum distance within which the direction of saturation can reverse is that for which H_D at the transition boundaries just reaches its critical threshold value for $M = M_r$. For digital magnetic recording we desire this distance x_1 to be small. The factor x_1 then represents a figure of merit of the recording medium.

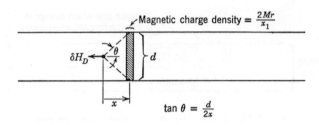

Fig. 5.15. Demagnetizing field from a track cross section within transition region.

Figure 5.15 shows the contribution to the field H_D arising from a differential strip dx at a distance x. For a uniformly charged strip the magnetic field contribution at a given distance is proportional to the subtended angle, 2θ. (Recall that the strip is infinite in length.) The magnetic field intensity is then obtained by integration over x_1. This field is the demagnetizing field H_D, which here will be considered only at the centerplane of the recording medium. If the indicated calculations are carried out, we get as a first order approximation

$$\frac{H_D}{M_r} = -N = -\frac{2}{\pi}\tan^{-1}\left(d/2x_1\right) \tag{5.31}$$

For $x_1/d \to 0$

$$\tan^{-1}\left(d/2x_1\right) \approx \pi/2$$

and hence $N = 1.0$. This checks with the previous result obtained for a perfect step change in magnetization (that is, $x_1 = 0$). As x_1 is increased, it is observed that N decreases rapidly. $N = 0.5$ for $x_1 = d/2$.

The point of magnetic equilibrium (Fig. 5.12) swings rapidly toward M_r as N approaches zero. Thus a small but finite x_1 permits stable zones of opposed saturation. For the magnetic oxide coating mentioned previously ($H_c = 250, B_r = 500$), which has an approximately rectangular hysteresis loop, the maximum permissible value for N is about $H_c/B_r = 0.5$ if the surface is to support saturated cells. Then for this material the saturation reversal width x_1 must be greater than $d/2$, one half the recording medium thickness, to assure stable saturated regions between magnetization changes. Theoretically then, the maximum density of saturation reversals $1/x_1$, based solely on the self-demagnetization phenomenon, less than $2/d$.

For cobalt-nickel, which has a much larger value of M_r, N must be much smaller than 0.5, since the maximum supportable demagnetizing field is not greatly different from that for the above oxide (that is, here typically $H_c \approx 200$ oersteds). Then for cobalt-nickel x_1 is considerably greater than d.

One conclusion from this highly simplified analysis is that the minimum saturation reversal distance is reduced as the recording surface thickness is reduced (see equation 5.31). This fact, in conjunction with the cited relative differences between cobalt-nickel and iron oxide in magnetic properties, would qualitatively explain why it is necessary with Co-Ni platings to use much thinner surfaces in order to achieve pulse resolutions comparable to those from magnetic oxide media.

REFERENCES

1. "Field Measurements on Magnetic Recording Heads," D. L. Clark and L. L. Merrill, *Proceedings of the IRE*, Vol. 35, pp. 1575–1579, December 1947.
2. *Magnetic Recording*, S. J. Begun, Rinehart and Co., New York, 1949.
3. "Mixed Ferrites for Recording Heads," R. Herr, *Electronics*, Vol. 24, pp. 124–125, April 1951.
4. "Recording Demagnetization in Magnetic Tape Recording," O. W. Muckenhirm, *Proceedings of the IRE*, Vol. 39, pp. 891–897, August 1951.
5. "Structure & Performance of Magnetic Transducer Heads," O. Kornei, *Journal Audio Engineering Society*, Vol. 1, No. 3, p. 225, July 1953.
6. "Magnetic Recorder of Electrical Impulses," R. G. Ofendengen, *Radiotekhnika*, Vol. 10, No. 11, pp. 65–79, 1955.
7. "Magnetic Data Recording Theory: Head Design," A. S. Hoagland, *Communication and Electronics (AIEE)*, pp. 506–512, November 1956.
8. "A Survey of Factors Limiting the Performance of Magnetic Recording Systems," E. D. Daniel, P. E. Axon, W. T. Frost, *Proceedings of the Institution of Electrical Engineers*, Part B, pp. 158–168, March 1957.
9. *Magnetic Recording Techniques*, W. E. Stewart, McGraw-Hill Book Company, 1958.
10. "High-Resolution Magnetic Recording Structures," A. S. Hoagland, *IBM Journal of Research and Development*, Vol. 2, No. 2, pp. 90–105, April 1958.
11. "Magnetic Characteristics of Recording Tapes and the Mechanism of the Recording Process," J. G. Woodward and E. Della Torre, *Journal Audio Engineering Society*, Vol. 7, pp. 189–195, 1959.
12. "High Density Magnetic Head Design for Noncontact Recording," L. F. Shew, *IRE Transactions on Electronic Computers*, Vol. EC-11, No. 6, pp. 764–772, December 1962.

6

DIGITAL RECORDING TECHNIQUES

In digital magnetic recording, the key performance criteria are the bit density in bits per inch (bpi) along a track and the track density in tracks per inch (tpi). The product of these two factors is the data storage density per square inch of the recording surface. The more effective the utilization of the storage surface area, the more favorable are the storage capacity to access time relationships associated with any given mechanical structure used for a data memory. Track density is predominantly only a function of mechanism tolerances and changes in this parameter imply major modifications in hardware composition and in mechanism design. Furthermore, not only does bit density significantly exceed track density, often by an order of magnitude or more, but it is the density parameter most susceptible to further major advances from progress in technology. Therefore, the performance factor of *greatest* interest in digital magnetic recording is bit density. Quite appropriately, bit density truly reflects the fundamental magnetics aspects of digital magnetic recording.

In the previous chapters we have dealt at some length with the overall magnetic recording process and the relation of the pulse recording resolution to the magnetic recording system parameters. The overall recording resolution can only be related to bit density, however, through the digital recording techniques used to store the binary information on writing and reconstruct this binary data from the output waveform on reading. Therefore this chapter will extend the previous developments and treat the basic principles and unique facets of digital magnetic recording techniques for binary data. The characteristics of the digital magnetic recording process will then be directly related to bit-storage density.

A fundamental feature of digital magnetic recording is the automatic, precise, and quantitative measure of performance reliability, as differentiated from other applications of magnetic recording. Each recorded bit is individually detected and interpreted, providing a continuing check on every region of the storage surface. The objective of achieving a high data storage density always involves striking a balance between bit density per se and the associated recording reliability. For this reason, some bit redundancy is generally included in the binary data to provide a degree of automatic error detection and correction. This subject is treated later in this chapter to identify the relation between the bit-density characteristics of a digital magnetic recording memory and computer techniques to enhance the operational performance of mass storage systems.

A magnetic recording system can be viewed as a communications channel. If we ignore the time delay between the writing and reading of a given information block, caused by the motion time necessary to permit re-scanning this section of track, we have essentially an input/output data-transfer channel (Fig. 6.1). This perspective is instructive, for it provides a familiar reference point and furthermore will

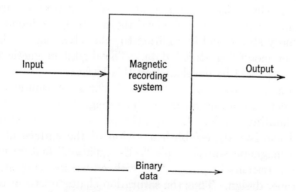

Fig. 6.1. Digital magnetic recording channel.

clearly reveal the unique aspects of the digital magnetic recording process in binary signal "transmission". The characteristics of the digital magnetic recording "channel" will be first elaborated, leading up to a discussion of digital recording techniques. The objective of this chapter is to provide an insight into the subject of digital recording techniques rather than merely a compilation of methods that have been used.

THE DIGITAL MAGNETIC RECORDING CHANNEL

The general aspects of binary magnetic recording and the consequent characterization of the digital magnetic recording channel are presented in this section. The relation between write current and output voltage will be generalized to cover the recording of binary input sequences. Noise sources are discussed under Readback Detection Techniques.

Qualitative Features of Binary Recording

Data in digital magnetic recording is coded in a binary notation. For example, in the binary coded decimal (BCD) code, a six would be written as 0 1 1 0. Our interest here, then, is specifically in the recording (writing and reading) of arbitrary sequences of ones and zeros. Frequently recording is done in parallel on a group of tracks, but the nature of the data signals associated with any single given track is still characterized by varying patterns of ones and zeros.

Only two unique states of magnetization are thus necessary for the storage of digital data. The unit of information is the bit and its two possible values, 0 or 1, may be directly represented by these two basic magnetic states (or the two types of transitions that are consequently associated with them), or by unique combinations formed from these basic states. Generally, two opposing senses of saturation are used in digital magnetic recording to achieve the maximum differentiation between memory states, and in addition to take advantage of the natural simplicity of modifying stored data. The digital magnetic recording channel concept will be developed on this basis.

Saturation recording exploits the non-linear saturation characteristic of the magnetic recording medium. The magnetic surface provides an inherent "limiting" action, through the phenomenon of saturation, to define and consistently establish a region of the surface at either of two stable magnetic states. This "self-regulating" feature can occur, even with variations in parameters such as writing current, spacing, etc., by proper design. Thus the saturation characteristic of the digital magnetic recording "channel" can be favorably exploited. The usual concept of "linearity" of the recording process has no relevance under such conditions, and one cannot directly speak of a correspondence between channel output and input in an analogy to conventional signal-transmission media.

The input current waveform on writing may be continuous, and if so, it will be constant in magnitude and will alternate in polarity ($I = \pm I_s$, where I_s is the saturation current). The writing current could otherwise consist of positive and negative current pulses of amplitude I_s. (Should the recording current saturate the track in one direction except when pulsed, only one polarity of current pulse is necessary.) Figure 6.2 gives examples of these three types of input current waveforms. It will prove useful to make a distinction between the smallest interval of unidirectional current, hereafter called a cell, and a data bit which may include more than one such cell. A cell also then defines the interval

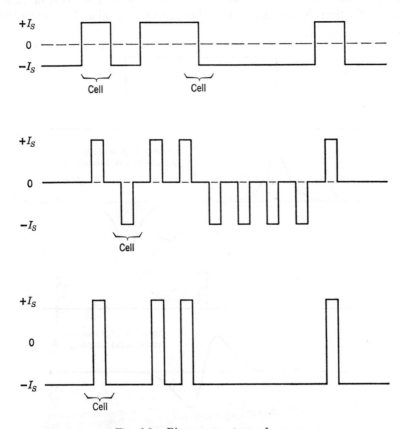

Fig. 6.2. Binary current waveforms.

uniquely allotted per current reversal with a continuous write current, as indicated in Fig. 6.2.

The output voltage waveform for a step change in current is a pulse, as described in Chapter 4 and illustrated in Fig. 6.3. A continuous writing current waveform (with binary recording) is composed of a succession of alternating step-like changes in current. Therefore, the associated output voltage waveform will inherently consist of an alternating pulse sequence (Fig. 6.3). Thus, the maximum value of the output signal will be given by the peak amplitude of the basic voltage pulse from a single current reversal. A continuous current mode for writing is predominantly used in digital magnetic recording practice.

For a current pulse, the output voltage signal will be a dipulse, as shown in Fig. 6.3. This waveform arises because a single current pulse records a discrete cell on the surface, having two closely spaced but oppositely directed magnetization transitions at its edges. One of these magnetization changes arises from the trailing leg field and one from the

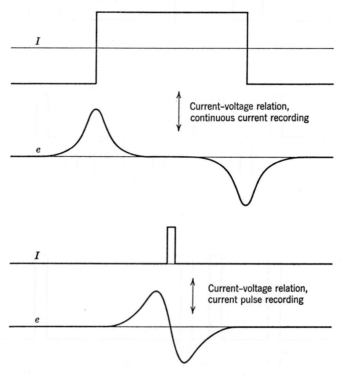

Fig. 6.3. Current-voltage relations, digital magnetic recording.

leading leg field of the magnetic head. The magnetization change produced by the leading leg of the head is a consequence of the turn off of the write current with each pulse (this phenomenon was discussed in Chapter 4). A dipulse signal would be anticipated, according to the general theory developed in previous chapters, from the superposition of two immediately adjacent pulses of opposite polarity, corresponding to the two magnetization reversals produced. However, here the separation of the magnetization reversals is fixed by the head-surface geometry as well as the period between current switchings (pulse duration).

The Characteristic Voltage Pulse

In Chapter 4 (equation 4.20) the following formula was derived, giving the relation between the output voltage signal and the recorded magnetization (it is assumed that $M = M_x(x)$ and is uniform throughout the recording layer d). An assumption, previously justified, which is implicit in this model analysis is that H_x is functionally independent of M_x.

$$e_x(\bar{x}) = KvN \int_{\delta}^{\delta+d} \int_{-\infty}^{+\infty} H_x(x, y) \frac{\partial M_x(x - \bar{x})}{\partial \bar{x}} \, dx \, dy \qquad (6.1)$$

Now setting

$$\frac{\partial M_x}{\partial \bar{x}} = M_x' \qquad (6.2)$$

and since typically the following approximation will be valid

$$H_x(x, y) \approx H_x(x, \delta + d/2) \quad \text{for} \quad \delta < y < \delta + d$$

we can write

$$e(\bar{x}) = KvNd \int_{-\infty}^{+\infty} H_x(x) M_x'(x - \bar{x}) \, dx \qquad (6.3)$$

In this form, $e(\bar{x})$ is expressed by a convolution integral. Then H_x can be regarded as a weighting function applied to an excitation function M_x'. In this sense, H_x is similar to an aperture or "window" by which M_x' is scanned. The voltage $e(\bar{x})$, as previously demonstrated, is identical in form with H_x for a step change in M_x. The parameter η has been used already to designate the spread of the magnetic head fringing field (H_x). η is a measure of the resolving power of the magnetic head, that is, a head with a reading resolution of η can individually resolve step changes in saturation magnetization up to a lineal density of $1/\eta$. For any magnetization pattern, in the limit as H_x approaches an impulse, that is, $\eta \to 0$ (corresponding to infinite resolving power), then,

$$e(\bar{x}) \to K_1 M_x' \qquad (6.4)$$

where K_1 is a constant. That is, the output voltage in waveform approaches the derivative of the recorded magnetization.

An additional parameter involved in specifying the overall recording resolution is x_1, the actual transition distance between two opposite directions of saturation. The basic mathematical approximation to M_x' for this transition region is shown in Fig. 6.4. The M_x' function is a rectangular pulse of amplitude $2M_r/x_1$ and width x_1. This magnetization pulse area, of course, must be equal to $2M_r$. x_1 then represents the minimum output voltage pulse width obtainable, even with infinite resolving power. In practice, η is finite and further $x_1 < \eta$. Therefore, the parameter η primarily sets the output pulse width and x_1 causes only a fractional increase in the readback pulse width (and decrease in the pulse amplitude) predicted on the basis of a true step change in magnetization.

In order to treat digital recording techniques mathematically, it is desirable to analytically describe the characteristic output voltage response to an impulse in M_x', corresponding to a step change in the direction of recording medium saturation. This characteristic voltage pulse will be seen to represent the fundamental "building block" for digital magnetic recording techniques. We have already discussed one expression that is a useful waveform approximation, particularly for

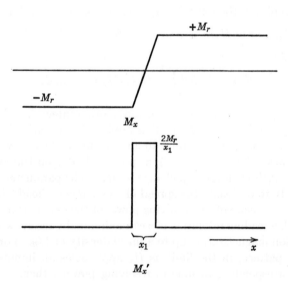

Fig. 6.4. Magnetization model for saturation reversal zone.

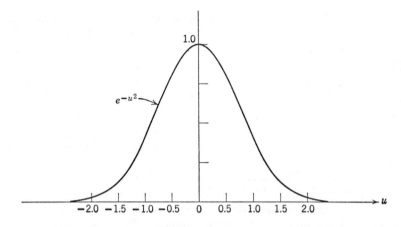

Fig. 6.5. "Gaussian" pulse response waveform.

head spacings from the mid-plane of the recording layer greater than the size of the magnetic head gap. This "far zone" equation is

$$e(u) = H_x(u) = \frac{1}{1 + u^2} \tag{6.5}$$

where $u = \bar{x}/y'$. (Recall that $y' = \delta + d/2$.) The curve is given in Chapter 4, Fig. 4.5. Another curve which is very useful is the Gaussian or normal probability density function. This expression can generally provide a good to excellent fit to experimentally obtained characteristic voltage pulses. This waveform is shown in Fig. 6.5 and is given by

$$e(u) = H_x(u) = e^{-u^2} \tag{6.6}$$

In expression (6.6), $u = ax$ where a is a scale factor and

$$\int_{-\infty}^{+\infty} e(u) \, du = \sqrt{\pi} \tag{6.7}$$

The pulse skirts of this Guassian pulse decay much more rapidly than the term $1/(1 + u^2)$ as u increases. The Gaussian curve is therefore more bell-shaped and can serve as a suitable mathematical approximation for the "near zone" head gap field.

Pulse Superposition Theory

In digital magnetic recording there is a wide array of recorded patterns, related to the variety of binary sequences that may be stored. We are hence dealing with a multitude of output voltage waveforms

arising from the possible alternating sequences of saturation magnetization changes. The *readback* process can be considered linear, as discussed previously. Thus the principle of superposition can be applied.
The net voltage (or flux) caused by a sequence of saturation changes on
the recording medium is then obtained by the linear combination of their
individual voltage (or flux) contributions. The utilization of the principle of superposition will be valid as long as the density of saturation
reversals does not exceed approximately $1/x_1$, the limit for the writing of
independent saturation reversals. With a separation between current
reversals of less than x_1, a magnetic transition region would be modified
by the reversed writing field established for an immediately subsequent
magnetization change. At this point the non-linear nature of the writing process would invalidate the description of the input-output relations
in terms of a characteristic pulse response. However, since $\eta > x_1$,
typically by a factor of five or greater, the performance limits set by the
reading resolution occur well before a density is reached at which the
use of superposition for waveform analysis becomes questionable. We
can therefore directly synthesize the spectrum of output voltage waveforms that must be correctly read as a function of bit density. We shall
use the symbol η' to define the voltage pulse width from an actual reversal in saturation magnetization, reserving η for the width of H_x
($\eta' \equiv \eta$ when $x_1 = 0$).

Figure 6.6a shows the read voltage e_1 (the subscript 1 will be used to
distinguish the waveforms synthesized from the characteristic voltage
pulse from this basic pulse signal itself) for a constant linear density of
saturation reversals. The parameter h defines the cell length, that is,
the minimum spacing between current reversals. In this instance, the
number of cells or pulses per inch (ppi) = $1/h$. Figure 6.6b gives a
curve of the peak output voltage versus ppi, obtained by the principle
of superposition. Several observations may be made. If each pulse is
to have its individual integrity preserved,

$$h \gtrsim \eta'$$

or

$$(\text{ppi})_{\max} = 1/\eta' \tag{6.8}$$

The output voltage peak amplitude will remain constant until adjacent
pulse interference extends to the pulse centers (see insert Fig. 6.6). (The
superposition of adjacent pulses is subtractive.) Therefore the "breakpoint" or fall-off point in the voltage curve (given in Fig. 6.6b) occurs at
approximately

$$\text{ppi} = 2/\eta' \tag{6.9}$$

The precise shape of the amplitude roll-off (ppi $> 2/'\eta$) will depend on

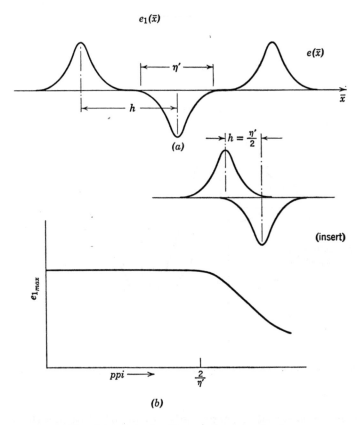

Fig. 6.6. Output voltage versus pulse density.

the actual waveform of the voltage pulse. If the pulse response, from an isolated current reversal, has a sharp peak and broad skirts, the amplitude drop-off will be gradual; for a characteristic pulse which is more bell-shaped, the amplitude roll-off curve will drop much more rapidly. This response curve can be thought of as being analogous to the normal frequency response curve giving a voltage versus frequency characteristic where cycles per inch (cpi) $= \frac{1}{2}$ (ppi).

Pulse Crowding—Examples. In digital recording a large number of output pulse patterns arise. At low densities each pulse is individually resolved. With higher densities pulse crowding (or inter-symbol interference) occurs. The consequent signal distortion that arises will be illustrated for several selected cases. These examples are "worst case" for specific forms of waveform distortion.

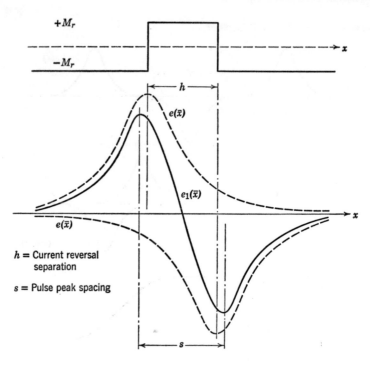

Fig. 6.7. Two adjacent saturation reversals and resultant signal showing peak shift effect.

(a) *Two adjacent saturation reversals.* Figure 6.7 illustrates the output signal when there is an isolated pair of saturation changes separated by a distance h appreciably less than η'. The individual signal from each saturation reversal is shown as well as the resultant voltage, obtained by the superposition of the individual pulses.

As seen in Fig. 6.7, there is a peak shift effect produced by pulse interference, indicated by the fact that the separation between the peaks of the output voltage is greater than h, the separation between the corresponding reversals in write current. This peak displacement phenomenon gives rise to a discrepancy in pulse location timing with respect to the original clock time period on writing (that is, h/v).

For any characteristic pulse waveform, the pulse separation s in the output waveform from two current reversals will approach a finite lower limit as h approaches zero. The signal $e_1(\bar{x})$ is obtained by the subtraction of the characteristic pulse e, offset by the distance h, from itself. This procedure amounts to an approximation method for differentiation of this reference pulse through a finite difference technique (excluding the division of the result at each point by h). Then as $h \to 0$

$$e_1(\bar{x}) \to h \cdot e'(\bar{x}) \qquad (6.10)$$

where

$$e'(\bar{x}) = \frac{de(\bar{x})}{d\bar{x}}$$

The signal $e'(\bar{x})$ is a dipulse, and the separation of its pulse peaks is obtained by setting $e''(\bar{x}) = 0$, that is, the derivative of $e'(\bar{x})$ with respect to $\bar{x}$.

Consider, for example, the following characteristic voltage pulse:

$$e(\bar{x}) = \frac{1}{1 + \bar{x}^2} \qquad (6.11)$$

If this calculation is carried out we obtain 1.15 as an answer; 1.15 is then the minimum value of s for the assumed characteristic pulse, where η' is approximately 6. The peak shift phenomenon is quite sensitive to the character of the peak of the basic readback pulse, a cusp-like waveform minimizing this effect.

As h becomes smaller the output signal amplitude will approach zero, but the separation between the two pulse peaks, corresponding to the recorded saturation reversals, approaches a finite limit. This situation is shown in Fig. 6.8. The onset of a peak shift begins as h decreases

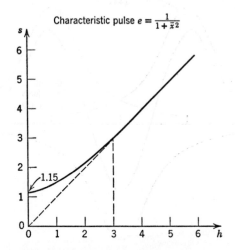

Fig. 6.8. Peak shift displacement s versus current reversal interval h.

below $\eta'/2 \approx 3$. As illustrated by Fig. 6.8, interpulse interference has a significant effect on the pulse timing with a continued reduction in h. For $h > 3$ (in this example) the output pulse separation is identical to the interval between current reversals or no peak shift problem arises.

(b) *Three adjacent saturation reversals.* Figure 6.9 shows the output waveform resulting from three adjacent saturation reversals when there is pulse crowding. Two effects are immediately obvious. First, the central pulse suffers a relatively greater attenuation than the other pulses. The amplitude of the center pulse peak is

$$e_1 = e(0) - 2e(\bar{x} = h) \tag{6.12}$$

In fact, this particular sequence is especially unfavorable to the amplitude of the central pulse. If an additional pulse were located on either end or on both ends of this pattern, their individual signal contributions would tend to increase the amplitude of this center pulse since they would both be negative (owing to the inherent alternating nature of successive

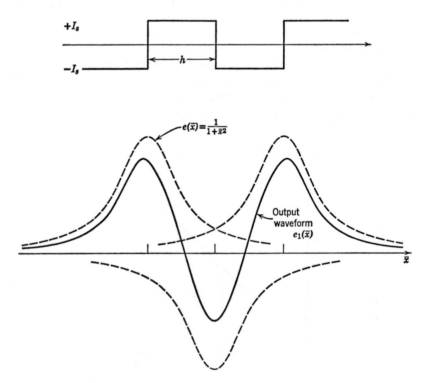

Fig. 6.9. Output signal from three adjacent saturation reversals.

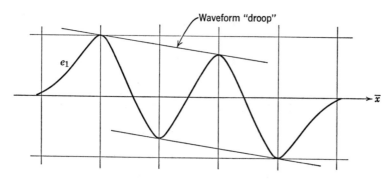

Fig. 6.10. Output signal from four successive saturation reversals.

pulses in saturation recording).   A second point that can be noted is the shifted base-line of the resultant signal.   The readback signal undergoes a positive displacement through the central region of the output waveform. e_1 exhibits a d-c component over this pulse grouping because of the odd pulse count.

(c) *Four successive saturation reversals.* Figure 6.10 shows the output signal with pulse crowding when four successive saturation reversals are recorded.   In this case, because of symmetry, the two outer pulses are of the same amplitude and the two inner pulses are also equal in magnitude.   The inner pulses are each surrounded by two adjacent pulses of opposite polarity and therefore are reduced in peak amplitude to a greater degree than the pulses on the waveform extremities.   The net effect is to give the waveform the appearance of a "droop" as shown. It is clear that here also there is base-line shift.

Pulse Interference—General Aspects.   The interval extending $h/2$ on both sides of a current reversal (in time the interval $\Delta t = h/v$) is the length uniquely allotted to this switching change.   This interval can also be identified, in terms of the associated output signal, as extending $\pm h/2$ on either side of the peak of the pulse $e(\bar{x})$.   The readback voltage waveform $e_1(\bar{x})$, during such an interval (or time slot), will be gradually distorted by the presence of neighboring saturation reversals, once the separation h between adjacent step reversals in write current is decreased below η'.   The actual voltage waveform in the "slot" assigned to a possible pulse position (clock period) will depend on the particular pattern of saturation reversals recorded in its immediate environment. Figure 6.11 shows the number of unique binary patterns leading to distinct waveforms in the interval h, when pulse interference extends to include the two nearest neighboring pulses that may be present on either

0	0	1	0	0	
0	1	1	1	0	
1	1	1	1	1	Equivalent binary configurations
1	0	1	0	1	
0	0	1	0	1	= 1 0 1 0 0
0	0	1	1	0	= 0 1 1 0 0
0	0	1	1	1	= 1 1 1 0 0
0	1	1	0	1	= 1 0 1 1 0
0	1	1	1	1	= 1 1 1 1 0
1	1	1	0	1	= 1 0 1 1 1

1 = Saturation reversal
0 = No change in current

Fig. 6.11. Unique saturation reversal combinations about given current switching point (considering two nearest neighbors on both sides).

side of the given pulse. In this case, there are ten distinct waveforms. As the degree of pulse crowding is increased, the number of different signals that will be encountered in a given cell interval h goes up rapidly. Because of the validity of the application of the principle of superposition, these waveforms, for any given value of h, can be generated or synthesized directly by graphical or numerical techniques from the characteristic pulse $e(\bar{x})$. There is an identical number of still different output waveforms corresponding to the absence of a recorded pulse in a selected clock period. To distinguish the presence of a recorded magnetization reversal we must essentially be able to correctly and unambiguously classify all readback waveforms arising within a cell interval into the appropriate one of these two possible sets.

An expression for the degree of pulse interference may be obtained by reference to Fig. 6.12. For a saturation reversal located n intervals distant from the point in question

$$nh - \eta'/2 \leqq h/2 \tag{6.13}$$

is the inequality relating h and η' which determines whether the output signal from this magnetization change will interfere with the signal in

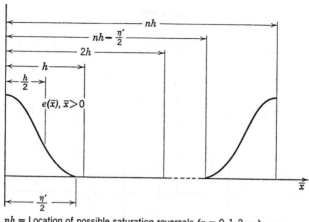

nh = Location of possible saturation reversals ($n = 0, 1, 2 \cdots$)
η' = Pulse spread (isolated saturation reversal)

Fig. 6.12. Pulse interference in terms of pulse width and pulse density.

the reference interval. For example, for $n = 3$,

$$h \approx \eta'/5$$

or

$$1/h = \text{ppi} \geqq 5/\eta' \qquad (6.14)$$

The "breakpoint" on the $(e_1)_{\max}$ versus ppi curve (Fig. 6.6) occurs at ppi $= 2/\eta'$. Thus we see that with pulse crowding of degree $n = 3$ we are far out on the roll-off curve, where appreciable amplitude reduction occurs.

WRITING (INPUT CURRENT ENCODING)

On writing, the two binary digits 0 and 1 must be converted into their respective states of magnetic surface saturation (and/or saturation reversals). We shall first consider digital recording methods where the writing current is continuous, by far the most frequently used approach. The techniques of coding the binary symbols using discrete write current pulses will be then presented.

NRZ Method

The most common method of writing is the NRZ (non-return to zero) technique. The relation between the binary data and the current (or surface magnetization) waveform for NRZ recording is illustrated in

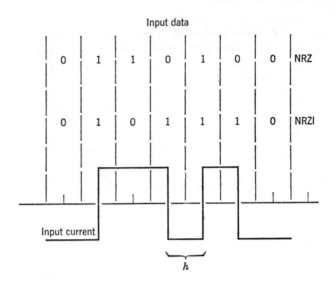

Fig. 6.13. NRZ and NRZI binary coding.

Fig. 6.13. The direction of writing current is reversed for every change in the binary sequence (1 followed by 0 or vice versa). Here, then, one direction of surface magnetization corresponds to a 1 while the opposite direction of magnetization corresponds to a 0. The so-called NRZI encoding method is essentially identical as concerns the digital magnetic recording process. In this scheme the current is reversed every time a 1 is to be recorded. A 1 signal will then be indicated by either a positive or a negative output pulse in the NRZI method of encoding and a 0 by the absence of a pulse. Also shown in Fig. 6.13 is the NRZI binary input sequence that gives the current waveform identical to that used to il-lustrate the NRZ recording method. These two methods are the same in their basic input-output signal characteristics, and therefore only one of these techniques, for this category of binary coding, needs to be ex-amined in any detail. The significance of the NRZI interpretation is that if a bit is misread only that bit is in error; with the NRZ system, if a bit is in error all succeeding bits will be erroneously read until the next signal pulse is encountered. Additional secondary advantages of NRZI compared to NRZ are: in parallel recording on a group of tracks an odd parity count per data frame (at least one bit must be a 1) guarantees a signal for readback timing per bit period; signal polarity is not a factor in interpreting the readback voltage, simplifying reading when bidirec-tional surface motion is used.

The NRZ recording method uses at a *maximum* one saturation reversal (or output pulse) per bit of information. This maximum occurs only when an alternating sequence of 1's and 0's is recorded. The NRZ scheme thus provides absolutely no redundancy in the input signal waveform. It would not be possible to encode the binary data with any fewer current (or magnetization) reversals (where all possible binary patterns are allowed). Not every bit is identified by a pulse, and therefore accurate clocking is necessary to correctly interpret the output waveform, particularly to read those data bits where a signal may not be sensed over several bit periods. In the NRZ method, bpi = $1/h$, and the maximum value of the output pulse density (ppi) is just equal to the recorded bit density.

Phase Modulation

The next binary coding technique to be described is variously referred to as the phase modulation method, the frequency modulation method, the Ferranti method, the double-frequency technique, and a few other more infrequently used terms. The term phase modulation will be used here to identify this basic digital recording technique. This method also involves a continuous writing current. Figure 6.14 illustrates the relationship between binary input data and the associated write current waveform for a typical binary pattern. A "1" is written, for example, by a positive change in writing current at data clock time, while a "0" would then be written by a negative change in saturation writing current. This coding procedure results in a "positive" read pulse for each recorded "1" and a negative read pulse for each "0." Regarding Fig.

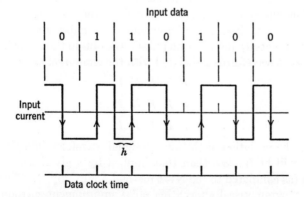

Fig. 6.14. Phase modulation binary coding.

6.14, it can be seen that an additional current reversal has to be inserted at mid-bit time when there are adjacent 1's or 0's, in order to meet these conditions. The additional output pulses that occur at these mid-bit times can be ignored in readback, being superfluous to the reconstruction of the original binary input sequence. This current coding technique can be viewed as a phase modulation process where a square wave, with one cycle per bit, has one phase for 1's and the opposite for 0's.

The phase modulation method provides more waveform redundancy than the NRZ method, since every data bit provides an output signal. Again, other current waveform identifications may be made for the binary digits with phase modulation coding (similar to the NRZI variant of NRZ), but the particular code and signal properties illustrated here are generic of this class of recording techniques. With phase modulation recording, the discrimination between a 1 and 0 involves in principle only detection of pulse polarity. The maximum number of input current reversals (or output pulses) per bit is equal to two, and in fact

$$\text{bpi} \leqq \text{ppi} \leqq 2 \text{ bpi} \tag{6.15}$$

where again bpi = bit density in bits per inch and ppi = output pulses per inch of track length (a variable which is dependent on the binary input data). Since both 0 and 1 bits provide read pulses, there is at least one output pulse per bit interval. This feature allows a clocking signal to be continuously generated from the output, advantageous for coping with bit synchronization problems in readout.

In phase modulation recording, the bit density is equal to $1/2h$. Thus, the phase modulation digital magnetic recording method will encounter pulse crowding before the NRZ method with increasing bit density. Examination of Fig. 6.14 reveals, however, that the number of pulse environments for a given bit signal is highly restricted in the phase modulation encoding technique. Consider the two nearest neighbor *pulse* locations on either side of a given output pulse, and let P = pulse (or current reversal) and N = no pulse. We obtain the following limited set of distinct waveforms associated with the chosen reference *bit* pulse.

$$P \; N \; \underline{P} \; N \; P$$
$$P \; P \; \underline{P} \; N \; P$$
$$P \; P \; \underline{P} \; P \; P$$

Therefore the variation of the output signal waveform in a given bit interval $2h$ will be far less than that implied by a given degree of pulse crowding (as compared to the NRZ method, for example). The presence of a nearly symmetrical alternating pulse environment surrounding any output pulse tends to minimize the problem of pulse location timing.

With the phase modulation technique every bit gives a pulse with its rise and fall sharply delineated by zero cross-over points, which are the best preserved waveform feature with considerable pulse interference. As shown in Fig. 6.14, the waveforms are also readily amenable to a-c coupling at both input and output.

RZ Method

RZ (return-to-zero) discrete pulse recording normally uses a pre-erased surface. A binary 1 is recorded by a very short current pulse, saturating a "spot" in one direction, while a 0 is stored as a "spot" saturated in the reverse direction. The RZ method is illustrated in Fig. 6.15. An input current pulse gives rise to a dipulse output signal. The readback signal indicating a 0 is an inverted 1 signal. Each bit records two magnetization transition zones, one by the leading edge of the gap and the other by the usual trailing gap field. The associated output signal is therefore broader than the pulse from a single current reversal. Pulse crowding will then occur at a lower bit density than it will for the NRZ method. For ideal step changes in magnetization, the positive and negative voltage peaks of the dipulse output would be only one-half the pulse amplitude obtained from NRZ recording, since here $\Delta M = M_r$.

The nature of the output signal makes the zero cross-over points of the output dipulses the logical reference with regard to bit timing. This method is like the phase modulation method, in that it provides a readback signal per recorded bit. Without a pre-erase there can be a serious problem with precise timing in current pulsing in order to assure properly recording over obsoleted data. This pre-erase aspect represents a serious handicap for the RZ method.

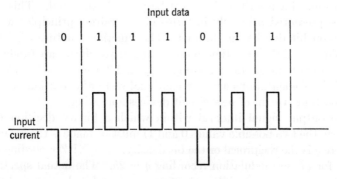

Fig. 6.15. RZ binary coding.

One advantage of the discrete pulse schemes, which may be important in some applications where high density is not an objective, is the ability to selectively write and thereby alter a single bit within a recorded sequence.

Biased Discrete Pulse Recording

In this type of digital recording, the surface is continuously saturated in one direction, except when a 1 is to be recorded. At such times a short current pulse, reversing the reference sense of saturation, is applied. Therefore, only recorded 1's provide output signals. This scheme has an advantage over the RZ method in that pre-erasure of the surface is never required. Again, like the RZ method the standard output dipulse is broader than the pulse from a single step change of current and successive 1's will produce a similar degree of inter-bit interference with increasing density.

An unique aspect of this method of current pulse recording (as no pre-erasure is required) is that it permits data (bit by bit) to be read and altered by rewriting during the same pass, since the output dipulse can be sensed before its corresponding write pulse time (the zero crossover point). This "early" read results because the head fringing field extends both in front as well as behind the head gap. Thus, a bit signal is sampled before its clock write time and, depending on the associated logical processing during this delay, a pulsed current reversal (insertion of a 1) may or may not be applied at the midpoint of the bit period.

READBACK DETECTION TECHNIQUES

The reading operation in binary recording is concerned with the reconstruction of the original binary input data from the output voltage waveform. Each written bit must be properly detected. This subject will be presented primarily in terms of generalized principles with emphasis on bit density limitations. The functional nature of detection techniques and their relation to the readback waveforms are fundamental to the digital magnetic recording "channel," while specific electronic circuit implementations are in a continual state of evolution because of the constant stream of new circuit devices appearing.

The output signal interval within which a binary decision (choice between the two possible values 0 and 1) must be made is the bit interval q where q is the reciprocal of the bit density. For NRZ recording $q = h$, while for phase modulation recording $q = 2h$. The actual spectrum of waveforms for e_1 in the interval q, for any given bit density and recording method, is as we have seen highly dependent on the overall characteristics of the magnetic recording system and the current encoding technique. Whether or not various signal-processing transformations are employed for readout detection, the final stage of discrimination to establish the binary value of a bit will involve a threshold amplitude. We therefore need finally to relate the merits of the various detection methods to this final decision mechanism.

Clocking. Clocking of data refers to the defining of the boundaries (location) of each bit interval. There are two forms of clocking, external and self-clocking. External clocking relies on an external clock source to define each bit period. The utility of this method depends on the degree of synchronization between the data track and the external clock source. With parallel track recording every track in the group must be in bit synchronism. The suitability of an external clocking technique is a function of the relative magnitudes of the mechanical and electrical tolerances affecting pulse position compared to the size of the bit interval. As bit density is increased, q becomes progressively smaller, and hence the percentage variability in the timing synchronization between clock and data will increase correspondingly, for any given recording device. Extreme demands are then placed on the design of the mechanical structure if external clocking is to be feasible at higher recording densities. Consequently self-clocking actually permits a higher bit density, although this latter technique does not lead to as high a bit density as is theoretically obtainable were it possible to have an ideal externally clocked system (one where there would be no bit timing instabilities).

The term self-clocking is used to describe reading methods in which the basic clock is derived from the data itself. Since each recorded track then clocks itself, there is no inherent barrier to recording in parallel on a group of tracks. However, in order to bring the respective output bits from such a group of tracks into time alignment, de-skewing buffers may be required. "Skew" refers here to the lack of synchronization between simultaneously operating recording tracks. At high density, one track output signal may be several bits ahead of another in time. Therefore buffering is needed to hold the bits from each track until all those corresponding to the same bit frame are available.

The generation of a clock from the recorded data is greatly facilitated if an output signal is obtained during each bit interval. This feature permits resynchronization or re-phasing of the "clock" every bit time. Otherwise, the electronic clock can free-run for several bit periods, and during this time the clock and recorded information are effectively decoupled. With NRZ coding this is the situation, and to minimize the exposure to a drift between the data and electronic clock, limitations are often imposed on the allowed binary combinations within recorded sequences. Requiring a frequency of occurrence of 1's in the binary data train above a certain minimum with the NRZI scheme, for example, would place a maximum time limit on the resynchronization of the clock. At higher densities, the self-clocking limitations of NRZ recording become an increasingly more serious restriction on the applicability of this method. One advantageous aspect of phase modulation recording is that this recording technique does provide an output pulse (one or two) per bit period. Self-clocking still, of course, requires a reasonably uniform relative velocity between surface and head during reading. The time slot for the subsequent bit must be generated by the electronic clocking circuit under the stimulus of the present bit (a bit interval is q/v in time).

The RZ recording method, which at low densities provides completely independent and distinct signals for each 1 and 0, does possess a capability for almost completely asynchronous operation. This requirement is not frequently necessary and, in particular, would not normally compensate for the acceptance of the lower bit-density potential of RZ recording.

Noise Sources. The term "signal-to-noise" (or S/N) ratio in digital magnetic recording requires special clarification. The normal signal level compared to random or unpredictable noise is extremely high. However, there are sources of signal distortion and amplitude variation that do effectively introduce serious problems in detection reliability.

The most common cause of readback failures are "dropouts." A dropout is a temporary loss of signal strength, caused by a transient increase in head-to-surface spacing, which is sufficient to cause reading errors. The sources of spacing fluctuations are found in particles (dust or loose surface material) that pass between the head and recording medium and in mechanical mounting dynamics. The sensitivity of the output pulse amplitude and pulse waveform to spacing has been previously described. At higher densities, where pulse crowding occurs, these transient changes in the waveform can negate the use of automatic gain control to compensate for amplitude reduction. Not only is there a very rapid attenuation of the readback signal with increasing spacing but the ability to write also undergoes a pronounced deterioration.

Variations in surface thickness also give rise to amplitude changes with track position, causing a reduction in the effective S/N ratio. Thus, along a track the input-output transfer relation varies, reducing the "overall" signal-to-noise ratio below that of any given storage location. This factor is steadily becoming less important because of continued advances in the process control operations connected with recording surface preparation.

Surface imperfections represent a "noise" source unique to magnetic recording. These imperfections can be foreign matter in the recording medium or the absence of recording material because of scratches, pin holes, etc. This extraneous signal source is "permanent" with respect to the surface. Although such defects are extremely rare, they must be anticipated. One procedure to circumvent this problem is to mark the boundaries of such an area by pulses and use these signals to skip over the defective section. Obviously, this must be an infrequent operation to maintain an effective level of performance.

A base-line "ripple" may arise from a residual signal, because of an inability to properly re-record over some section of a track (and thereby obliterate entirely the previous magnetization history). This type of signal may also result from a surface whose magnetization varies with position because of a coarse microstructure, even though it is uniformly magnetized.

Noise impulses can be introduced into the reading electronics by electric signals coupling with the magnetic head coil and leads. Electrical noise spikes are generally eliminated by inserting in the output a filter which will just accommodate the frequency band contained in the readback signal.

In practice, generally the S/N ratio in the communications theoretic sense is quite high, and the basic bit density limitations in digital magnetic recording stem from intersymbol interference, compounded by signal waveform perturbations arising from spatial parameter variations.

NRZ(I) Recording

Amplitude Sensing. The most direct method of reading NRZ waveforms is simply to amplitude-sense the output voltage. Consider the NRZI code. We choose a threshold voltage e_T and, by sampling the output signal at the center of each bit interval, we can define the value of the output in terms of e_T as follows:

$$e_T > e_1 \quad \text{output} = 0$$
$$e_T \le e_1 \quad \text{output} = 1$$

We shall assume that there is an accurate clock source for sampling the output voltage at the center of each bit interval. Furthermore, the peak amplitude of the characteristic pulse will be considered normalized to 1.0, that is, $e(\bar{x} = 0) = 1.0$.

The largest "0" signal will result from the worst case pattern, $...000\underline{0}100...$ (where the underline indicates the particular bit under investigation). Then

$$e_1|_{\max} (\text{``0''}) = e(\bar{x} = q) \tag{6.16}$$

At low densities where $q > \eta'$, this "0" voltage is equal to or very near zero. As q becomes less than $\eta'/2$, the "0" signal begins to rise significantly. In order to read this "0" correctly, e_T must be greater than $e(\bar{x} = q)$. The minimum "1" signal will occur with the worst case pattern ...0011100... Here the adjacent 1 pulses subtract from the "1" signal of concern. Then

$$e_1|_{\min} \ (\text{"1"}) = 1 - 2e(\bar{x} = q) \tag{6.17}$$

This voltage is approximately equal to 1 until $q < \eta'/2$, at which point the adjacent pulses begin to reduce the peak signal of the central "1" pulse markedly. e_T must be less than $e_1|_{\min}$ ("1") in order to read this pulse properly as a 1 bit.

Now it is necessary that

$$e_1|_{\min} \ (\text{"1"}) \geq e_1|_{\max} \ (\text{"0"})$$

to correctly discriminate 1's from 0's with amplitude detection. It is seen that e_T must fall within these two voltage bounds, which in turn are a function of the degree of pulse crowding and hence bit density.

The theoretical bit-density limit can be found by substituting and equating the voltages corresponding to these two limits. That is, setting

$$1 - 2e(\bar{x}) = e(\bar{x}) \tag{6.18}$$

where here $\bar{x} = q_{\min}$. Then, $e(q_{\min}) = \frac{1}{3}$. For $q = q_{\min}$, the maximum zero signal is equal to the minimum one signal and correct bit discrimination is no longer possible. Further, since $\text{bpi}_{\max} = 1/q_{\min}$, then at this bit-density limit, e_T must equal $\frac{1}{3}$.

To determine signals margins and density limitations with this simple amplitude detection method we must choose a specific waveform function for $e(\bar{x})$. Let, for example,

$$e(\bar{x}) = \frac{1}{1 + (\bar{x})^2}$$

This characteristic pulse has its amplitude normalized to 1.0 and its pulse width to $\eta' = 6$ and has been seen to be a common form of approximation. We can now solve for $q_{\min}$ by setting

$$\frac{1}{1 + q^2} = \frac{1}{3} \tag{6.19}$$

We get

$$q_{\min} = 1.4$$

or

$$\text{bpi}_{\max} = 0.7$$

(In this example, for an actual characteristic pulse width of three thousandths of an inch the conversion factor for density is $6/3 \cdot 10^{-3}$ or $2 \cdot 10^3$.) Since $2/\eta' = 0.33$, the maximum density limit is slightly greater than twice the bit density at which the peak amplitude of a sequence of ones begins to fall noticeably (Fig. 6.6). Figure 6.16 illustrates graphically the variation of $e_1|_{max}$ ("0") and $e_1|_{min}$ ("1") with bit density for this particular characteristic pulse. The shaded band designates the acceptable range for e_T as a function of bit density.

In practice, to allow for parameter variations and provide reliability, one could not actually expect to record up to this bit density limit. Given specified signal tolerances one could, from curves like those in Fig. 6.16, establish both the maximum usable density and the optimum setting for e_T. In addition to output amplitude imposed limitations on density, the direct sensing of signal amplitude for bit detection causes large variations in timing with self-clocking, which as stated previously is a frequent clocking requirement because of the mechanical tolerances encountered. This situation occurs since the fixed threshold voltage is then the only basis on which to fix pulse location. Every time $|e_1|$ crosses over the threshold, the presence of a pulse is recognized and the

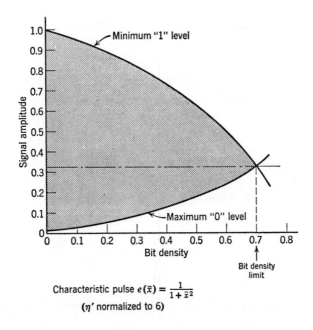

Characteristic pulse $e(\bar{x}) = \dfrac{1}{1 + \bar{x}^2}$

(η' normalized to 6)

Fig. 6.16. Threshold detection limits for amplitude sensing (NRZI coding).

clock timing is resynchronized in some prescribed manner from this time instant. However, the intersection of e_1 with e_T will occur at varying positions along the leading edge of the output pulses as the signal waveform changes from pulse crowding or parameter fluctuations. Since this threshold crossing defines the location of the next bit interval, the generated clock will vary considerably from an optimum timing reference, which would be a clock directly locked to the saturation reversals.

Peak Sensing. For the reasons given, among others, it is worthwhile to examine the merit of a peak sensing technique for NRZ recording. This method circumvents absolute amplitude as a signal waveform factor.* The actual detection of a peak usually involves differentiation, high gain amplification and limiting, and a reasonably low-level threshold detector. This series of waveform operations is shown in Fig. 6.17. This procedure provides a fairly accurate determination of pulse peak

* This ignores the fact that base-line clipping is generally used to reduce "noise."

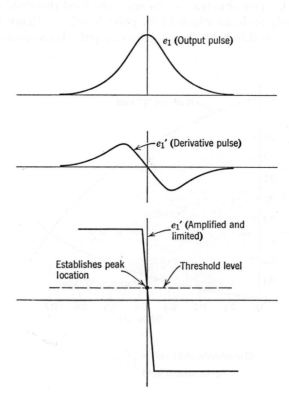

Fig. 6.17. Peak sensing.

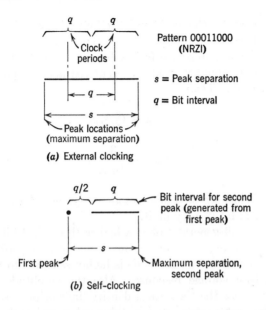

Fig. 6.18. Timing limitations in peak sensing (NRZ coding).

locations. For a non-perturbed readback waveform, pulse timing rather than pulse amplitude will determine bit-density performance.

With peak sensing, the "worst case" pattern is ...00011000.... As noted earlier, with increasing density two adjacent ones undergo a relative peak shift because of inter-bit interference.

First, for external clocking the limiting condition on q is shown in Fig. 6.18a. (At low densities $s = q$, where s is the peak separation and q the bit interval.) Since both resultant pulses are displaced relative to one another in a manner to increase pulse peak spacing, the two corresponding clock times (fixed) for these pulse peaks will both occur between the actual pulse peak signals. We can continue to decrease the current switching interval until the corresponding external clock period (q) will just fail to include the pulse peak. (These clock periods are optimally centered on the instants corresponding to undistorted readback peaks.) Then from Fig. 6.18a we see that

$$q_{min} = \frac{s_{min}}{2} \tag{6.20}$$

or

$$bpi_{max} = \frac{1}{q_{min}} = \frac{2}{s_{min}}$$

Let us also examine this limit under self-clocking conditions. Regard Fig. 6.18b. Here the lower limit on q occurs when the clock interval generated by the first pulse just fails to bracket the following pulse peak. This clock period would normally be centered about a point distant q from the first peak. Then

$$q_{min} = (\tfrac{2}{3})s_{min}$$

or

$$bpi_{max} = \frac{3}{2s_{min}} \tag{6.21}$$

The use of self-clocking then involves an acceptance of a 25% reduction in the theoretical bit density limit.

Peak sensing will generally offer a higher theoretical bit-density potential than direct amplitude detection. However, the performance differential between these two methods is highly sensitive to the shape of the characteristic voltage response. Also the amplitude loss due to pulse crowding near the theoretical density limit of peak sensing raises a consideration not encompassed in this analysis. Residual signals or voltage perturbations from surface irregularities have voltage peaks that, under the peak sensing waveform transformations, can give erroneous output "1" bits. To minimize this exposure it is usual to clip out the base-line signal band. This procedure immediately places amplitude restrictions on the reading signal which may be more limiting than those from peak shift in spite of peak sensing.

A major drawback to the NRZI type method is the lack of an output signal per bit. With either amplitude or peak sensing it is still necessary to insert the zeros properly through an accurate timing reference. Since the clock (with either self or external clocking) is decoupled from the data during the passage of zeros, this can be a difficult problem. Further, base-line shift and waveform distortions arising from variations in spacing serve to compound both the amplitude and peak-detection problems at higher densities. For these reasons phase modulation recording, to be discussed next, is used in the highest bit-density storage applications, even though it involves a more redundant recording signal.

Phase-Modulation Recording

Phase-modulation signals can be detected and decoded by both amplitude and peak sensing. A basic advantage inherent in the phase-modulation method, for reading, is the much more restrictive set of output waveforms encountered. Regarded from a pulse rate or frequency point of view we have with phase modulation recording

$$\text{bpi} \leq \text{ppi} \leq 2 \text{ bpi}$$

This pulse density pass band minimizes low-frequency base-line distortion. Further, deviations in pulse peak timing are minimized, since each pulse tends to have a very symmetrical environment. The fact that there is at least one pulse per bit gives an alternating waveform that tends to improve the definition of the signal peaks, since the pulse skirts fall more rapidly because of the subtractive influence of adjacent pulses.

For these reasons phase-modulation recording can be highly reliable, even under the adverse influence of spacing variations. With a large loss in voltage amplitude, the fact that there is an alternating "periodic" signal tends to preserve the readback data timing. The continuous train of recorded pulses, particularly for densities at which pulse crowding occurs, minimizes the noise from possible variations in magnetization (in uniformly saturated sections) because of an imperfect homogeneity of the surface layer. Since the waveform has each bit interval delineated by zero cross-over points, automatic gain control can be very successfully applied to counteract spacing and thickness changes. These advantages, along with its natural suitability to self-clocking, more than overcome the greater pulse interference effects (note that here $h = q/2$) and have made this recording technique the one principally exploited for high-density recording.

In considering density limitations with phase-modulation recording, it should be recognized that reliable detection at both of the limiting or instantaneous pulse densities ppi = bpi and ppi = 2 bpi is essential to derive the benefits of this recording technique. Figure 6.8 has indicated the increasingly rapid signal attenuation with ppi. For the equivalent sine wave response (assuming one cycle per inch approximates 2 ppi), we know that the readback voltage drops off exponentially with frequency. Therefore

$$\frac{e_1(\text{ppi} = 2 \text{ bpi})}{e_1(\text{ppi} = \text{bpi})} \rightarrow 0 \tag{6.22}$$

as the bit density is continuously increased. Since the ratio given by equation (6.22) is typically chosen to be no less than 0.5 (under standard recording conditions), to guarantee zero cross-over protection, this maximum for bit density can easily be projected from the $e_1(\text{ppi})$ curve. The high reliability of phase modulation recording makes it useful at very high densities where other recording methods, although technically capable of even higher densities, are not suited to the operational conditions of actual recording systems.

Discrete Pulse Recording

The fundamental output pulse with RZ recording is a dipulse. The zero cross-over point of this dipulse represents the center of the signal, and the direction of the waveform slope at this point carries the essential information on the binary digit that is stored. Therefore some form of slope sensing is necessary in signal detection.

Figure 6.19 shows the characteristic output voltage waveform for a discrete recorded pulse and the derivative of this signal. The derivative signal gives a positive or a negative pulse at the center of the original dipulse, reflecting the direction of the rate of change of voltage at the zero cross-over point. The derivative of the readback signal can then be used as a basic waveform to determine the recorded binary data. Only the polarity of this derivative voltage (in the middle of the bit interval) need be tested.

RZ recording normally implies relatively low density and stable timing, hence the unwanted signal during the remainder of the bit interval can be excluded by a narrow read strobe. Therefore these portions of the waveform, shown in Fig. 6.19, can be ignored. The rapid voltage change at the dipulse cross-over point results in a voltage pulse, in the

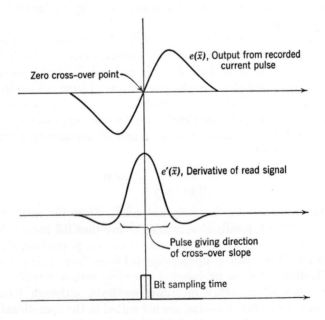

Fig. 6.19. Detection, discrete pulse recording.

derivative signal, appreciably larger than the remainder of the voltage output during the bit interval.

The unique features of the RZ type of recording discussed previously result only when there is little if any pulse crowding. Therefore RZ techniques are not pursued in a significant way for high-density recording.

ELECTRICAL COMPENSATION OF THE DIGITAL MAGNETIC RECORDING CHANNEL

We have seen that the readback output voltage can be expressed as follows:

$$e(\bar{x}) = K_1 \int_{-\infty}^{+\infty} H_x(x) M_x'(x - \bar{x})\, dx \qquad (6.23)$$

where $\bar{x}$ is the x coordinate location of the recorded magnetization pattern with respect to the gap center of the magnetic head, and M_x' is the x derivative of this longitudinal magnetization pattern. Now in this relation, $e(\bar{x})$ is expressed in the form of a convolution integral where $H_x(x)$ can be regarded as an impulse response function and $M_x'(x)$ as a system input signal. K_1 is a constant.

In digital magnetic recording it is valid to assume $H_x(x)$ is *not* a function of $M_x(x)$. We can then apply linear system theory and write (dropping the subscript x which is hereafter to be understood)

$$E(j\omega) = H(j\omega) M'(j\omega) \qquad (6.24)$$

$E(j\omega)$ is the Fourier transform of e, $H(j\omega)$ the Fourier transform of $H(x)$, and $M'(j\omega)$ the Fourier transform of $M'(x)$. In equation (6.24) the angular frequency

$$\omega = \frac{2\pi v}{\lambda} \qquad (6.25)$$

where λ is the recorded wavelength. Of greatest importance, the frequency spectrum here is only absolutely related to distance (and not time), since λ is a spatial parameter corresponding to a wavelength along the track coordinate x.

This perspective is suggestive of the time-frequency relations in linear circuit theory, and from this point of view, the recording operation can be represented in block diagram form in terms of transfer functions, as shown in Fig. 6.20a. From this communications viewpoint, it is noted that since the limits of the integral in equation (6.23) extend from minus infinity to plus infinity, this expression is not restricted to physically realizable "filters" of the electrical network variety. Since we have

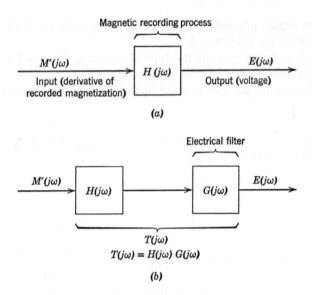

Fig. 6.20. Input-output transfer function block diagrams.

been defining $H(x)$ for $-\infty < x < +\infty$, and since in our analogy $\bar{x}$ (or x) corresponds to "time," we see that our impulse response transfer function provides an anticipatory output.

Now we can modify the input-output relation shown in Fig. 6.20a by insertion of an electrical filter at the head output. If the voltage at the input terminals of this filter is not disturbed by its presence, we can redraw the input-output transfer relation, as shown in Fig. 6.20b, where $G(j\omega)$ represents the frequency characteristic of the electrical filter. This situation will apply, for H_x represents the transfer function of the magnetic recording process, and the electrical parameters of the magnetic head can be viewed as incorporated into the design of the inserted filter. The input $M'(x)$ is then related to the output voltage $e(x)$ by the following transfer function:

$$T(j\omega) = H(j\omega)G(j\omega) \tag{6.26}$$

Theoretically, if $G(j\omega)$ could be chosen such that

$$H(j\omega)G(j\omega) \approx 1.0$$

over the read signal bandwidth, then $E(j\omega)$ would be identically equal to $M'(j\omega)$ or

$$e(\bar{x}) = M'(\bar{x})$$

Thus, in the limit, with complete compensation of the "readback channel," the overall digital recording performance would be set solely by the magnetization reversal distance on writing, x_1. Since the output pulse width caused by readback is considerably greater than x_1 (that is, $\eta' > x_1$), there is considerable merit in examining the potential gain in bit density that may be realized by electrical compensation (or equalization) of the digital magnetic recording channel.

Time Domain Factors

$G(j\omega)$ characterizes an electrical network in a frequency domain measured in terms of true time. However, we have seen that with respect to $M'(x)$ and $H(x)$ the frequency transformation gives a frequency variable equal to v/λ, where v is the relative velocity between head and surface and λ is a spatial wavelength of magnetization along the track. We must then set f (frequency in cycles per second) $= v/\lambda$. This implicit mixture of the time and space domains in the overall transfer function requires that the surface velocity v, within a very small percentage tolerance, remain constant. A slight change in speed will proportionately shift the frequency spectrums (in time) of $M'(x)$ and $H(x)$. $G(j\omega)$ is, of course, unaffected by variations in surface velocity. Thus, whenever v departs from its design value, the electrical filter $G(j\omega)$ will be no longer "matched" to the magnetic recording channel. The resulting frequency compensation under this condition is off-design. The output signal distortions which may result (particularly if appreciable speed changes occur) could actually degrade the overall performance of the compensated channel below that of the uncompensated system. This sensitivity to velocity is one major reason the "equalization" of the digital magnetic recording channel has not been exploited more intensively.

Furthermore, we shall see that the transfer function $H(j\omega)$ of the digital magnetic recording channel makes the realization of $G(j\omega)$ an approximation problem in network synthesis. The consequent limitations of filter design implementation also restrict the general utility and potential of the equalization concept for digital magnetic recording.

Analysis of Electrical Filter Compensation

To proceed with the analytic formulation of the relations between readback filter networks and pulse output (and thus bit density), we first must refine our representation of $M'(x)$. $M'(x)$ is zero everywhere except at a transition region between a change in direction of recording medium magnetization. We assume that $M'(x)$ is a constant throughout such an interval of width x_1. Therefore $M'(x)$ is approximated by a rectangular pulse of amplitude $2M_r/x_1$ and width x_1. Theoretically the minimum output pulse width from this magnetization change is equal to x_1, achievable if the fringing field function $H(x)$ could be completely compensated for by $G(j\omega)$. Now we have already seen qualitatively that $x_1 < \eta$, and experimentally it appears that $x_1 < 0.2\eta$. Thus the output voltage pulse in the absence of any equalization network is essentially completely determined by $H(x)$ alone. Further, as will be indicated shortly, even with electrical compensation of the digital magnetic recording channel, the feasible degree of pulse resolution improvement still tends to fall within pulse width range predominantly established by $H(x)$. Thus, we can safely assume that x_1 goes to zero and approximate $M'(x)$ by an impulse of magnitude $2M_r$ (that is, $2M_r$ is the area of the impulse function).

Then for the compensated channel, from equations (6.24) and (6.26),

$$E(j\omega) \propto T(j\omega) \tag{6.27}$$

or

$$e(\bar{x}) \propto T(\bar{x}) \tag{6.28}$$

For purposes of analytical exposition, let us take

$$H(x) = e^{-a^2 x^2} \tag{6.29}$$

This fringing field function is a Gaussian distribution curve. As previously mentioned, this general waveform can frequently be closely fitted to both field plots of H_x and experimentally obtained output voltage pulses. Further, its mathematical form makes it very amenable to design calculations. The corresponding characteristic voltage pulse (normalized to a peak amplitude of 1.0) will be

$$e = e^{-a^2 x^2}$$

Taking the Fourier transform of $H(x)$, we get

$$H(j\omega) = H(\omega) = \frac{\sqrt{\pi}}{a} e^{-\omega^2/4a^2} \tag{6.30}$$

Note that $H(\omega)$ is also a Gaussian function. The transform of $H(x)$ carries no phase information since $H(x) = H(-x)$. Now we can set as a design goal the insertion of a linear passive filter (plus linear amplifier) to obtain the following characteristic pulse output:

$$e = e^{-c^2 x^2} \tag{6.31}$$

This signal is of the same form and peak amplitude as the original pulse.

For $c > a$ the width of the pulse from the compensated channel is less than the pulse width of the original signal. Thus by choosing $c > a$ we will improve the reading resolution of the system. The principle of superposition is also valid here, for $G(j\omega)$ is a linear network. Since the basic output signal waveform has been retained, we can apply directly to the new characteristic output voltage the same analysis and evaluation criteria for the detection techniques previously discussed. Therefore, projections are straightforward on the bit-density gains that can be realized, with respect to limitations arising from interbit interference or pulse crowding. If the original output pulse is reduced in pulse width by 50%, then a 100% improvement in bit density is potentially possible with the same detection method.

For the "pulse slimming" output signal transformation just indicated we require

$$T(\omega) = H(\omega)G(\omega) = \frac{\sqrt{\pi}}{c} e^{-\omega^2/4c^2} \qquad (6.32)$$

$T(\omega)$ is functionally similar to $H(\omega)$ since we chose to preserve the shape of the original output pulse waveform. Then

$$G(\omega) = \frac{T(\omega)}{H(\omega)} = \frac{a}{c} e^{\left[\frac{(c^2-a^2)\omega^2}{4c^2a^2}\right]} \qquad (6.33)$$

The electrical network synthesis problem is concerned with the realization of $G(\omega)$. Figure 6.21 shows a graph of the function $G(\omega)$. $G(\omega)$ is

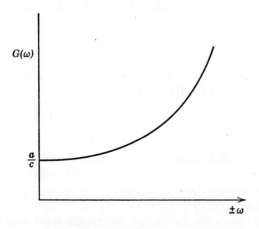

Fig. 6.21. Frequency characteristic of compensation network.

not physically realizable, and therefore we must approximate this frequency function over a finite bandwidth, for example, with a linear passive network plus a broad-band linear amplifier. The need for gain arises because in the formulation of the problem we chose to set the peak output amplitude of the compensated pulse at the same signal level as held before the introduction of the filter (that is, both voltage pulses are normalized to 1.0). Such a restoration of signal level is necessary before feeding into the detection circuitry.

An interrelation between output pulse width and signal-to-noise ratio is involved with this approach to increasing bit density. To clarify this relation we shall carry this analysis through a specific example. Suppose we attempt to halve the basic readback pulse width. Narrowing the pulse response to this degree offers a possibility for doubling the bit density. In this case

$$c = 2a \tag{6.34}$$

or

$$G(\omega) = \tfrac{1}{2} e^{3/4 \frac{(\omega^2)}{(4a^2)}} \tag{6.35}$$

To proceed further we must select a bandwidth criterion. In order to adequately reproduce a Gaussian voltage pulse we shall set $\omega = 0$ as the low-frequency limit and define the high-frequency cut-off as that frequency at which the relative amplitude (compared to the low-frequency range) of the Gaussian signal-frequency spectrum is down by a factor of e^{-1}. This bandwidth will include approximately 95% of the signal energy in this pulse. Specific design figures depend on the bandwidth definition used, but this criterion is a reasonable requirement and provides some simplicity in calculation. Then for $T(\omega)$ we have

$$\omega_c = 2c \tag{6.36}$$

where ω_c is then the high-frequency cut-off point. The uncompensated transfer function $H(\omega)$ would reach a relative attenuation of e^{-1} in its frequency response at the frequency

$$\omega = 2a = \omega_c/2 \tag{6.37}$$

Thus, we are effectively doubling the "bandwidth" of the overall input-output channel, which directly corresponds to our objective of reducing the output pulse width by a factor of 2. This simple relation holds since, with an impulse signal $M'(x)$ as the source input, the output pulse width is inversely proportional to the overall "filter" bandwidth.

Figure 6.22 shows the frequency spectrums $H(\omega)$ and $T(\omega)$ for this problem, the transformation of $H(\omega)$ into $T(\omega)$ being achieved by $G(\omega)$.

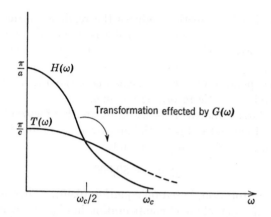

Fig. 6.22. Transfer function frequency characteristics.

Substituting $c = 2a$ and $\omega = \omega_c = 2c = 4a$ in the equation for $G(\omega)$ given by equation (6.33), we get

$$G(\omega_c) = \tfrac{1}{2}e^3 \approx 10 \qquad (6.38)$$

Furthermore,

$$G(0) = 1/2 \qquad (6.39)$$

Note that we can now write

$$G(\omega) \approx \tfrac{1}{2}[20]^{(\omega/\omega_c)^2} \qquad (6.40)$$

where ω_c retains its earlier definition, that is,

$$\omega_c = 2c$$

$G(\omega)$ may consist of a passive filter network, approximating the desired inverse filter frequency response out to $\omega = \omega_c$, followed by an amplifier flat out to at least ω_c. The passive element circuit then attenuates the low frequencies ($\omega \approx 0$) relative to the high frequencies ($\omega \approx \omega_c$) by a factor of 20. A voltage gain of 10 is required to preserve signal amplitude.

The peak signal-to-rms noise ratio will be decreased through electrical compensation of the digital magnetic recording channel, representing a trade-off of S/N ratio for bandwidth. Assuming white noise, the output noise contribution arising from a noise source located at the input of $H(\omega)$ will be proportional to the square root of the bandwidth. For the example given, such a noise component would be increased by $\sqrt{2}$. The added amplifier will introduce an additional noise source that could be significant. Further, consider noise that may be introduced into the system at the magnetic head output terminals, that is, prior to $G(\omega)$.

While the passive filter section reduces the readback signal amplitude by a factor of roughly 10, this filter will pass a considerable percentage of the noise energy in the frequency band $0 < \omega < \omega_c$, particularly at the high-frequency end. The seriousness of the net reduction in signal-to-noise ratio depends on the margin existing in the original S/N ratio of the basic digital magnetic recording channel.

If we desired to extend the bandwidth by another factor of two by this technique, looking to a total potential improvement of four in bit density, we would require a gain of approximately

$$\tfrac{1}{2}[20]^4 = 80,000$$

for amplitude restoration, based on equation (6.40). Therefore, because of the nature of $G(\omega)$, channel compensation in digital magnetic recording for pulse width reduction can very rapidly degrade the signal-to-noise ratio if one attempts to secure much more than a factor of 2 improvement.

Electrical Compensation: Summary

The principal limitations that show up in the consideration of this technique will be briefly restated. The velocity v must be very stable to maintain proper compensation, since $H(\omega)$ is velocity dependent (ω is proportional to v) while $G(\omega)$ is a time domain filter and independent of the surface velocity. $G(\omega)$ is not physically realizable, and suitable filter approximations are fairly complex because of its particular frequency characteristic. Therefore, actual filters may give some base-line pulse distortion, such as overshoots, etc. This signal-waveform distortion may seriously impair the performance obtainable from the signal-detection stage. The filter approach is based on a given $H(x)$, and therefore any perturbations in spacing or the other spatial parameters will also disturb the matching of the inverse filter to the head-surface transfer function. Finally, a loss in S/N ratio must be accepted. While the signal-to-noise ratio is normally quite high, this ratio can be rapidly reduced as pulse width is decreased. However, this approach certainly merits consideration where high density is of prime importance.

RELIABILITY TECHNIQUES

In digital mass storage, there are several special techniques to improve overall performance reliability and thereby contribute to the practical utilization of higher bit densities. A parity check bit included within each recorded character (6 to 8 bits) is standard, to provide automatic error detection. The addition of more check bits is sometimes also used to secure single-bit error correction. When handling larger groups of bits (for example, a record consisting of 100 characters), more powerful checking techniques become efficient. Thus, burst error correction codes, utilizing checking characters at the end of an information block, are becoming of more and more interest. A burst error correcting code can correct up to a specified number of successive bits in error.

Redundant codes call for additional hardware and time (additional computer cycles) to store the additional data and execute the checks. To justify the use of some form of redundancy, the benefits must be balanced against and outweigh these needs. Normally, the decision is favorable to the use of redundancy to improve reliability, since data-processing systems involve such a complex of equipment and process data so rapidly that the loss of even a short period of useful time because of errors is extremely expensive.

Error detection and correction codes can contribute immensely to the operational performance of a magnetic mass store. These techniques are invaluable in contending with intermittent errors due to spacing fluctuations, etc. With higher densities, the burst error correcting codes become particularly attractive. For example, a dust particle, temporarily increasing the head-to-surface spacing, affects a given section of the track and may cause "dropout(s)." At lower densities this distance may correspond to a single bit, but at high bit densities an entire group of successive bits would be lost. Also, bit positions permanently unusable, for example, those caused by a surface scratch, can be tolerated if sufficient data redundancy is provided. However, it may be more desirable to mark the edges of such an area (by recording special signals) and skip over it, since otherwise the degree of error protection remaining for the track sections containing such defects is necessarily less.

With automatic error correction a memory system can continue to maintain full operational performance even in the face of bit errors. Automatic error detection provides a means for the data-processing system to immediately initiate programmed procedures, which can automatically attempt to rectify the error. One automatic procedure that is commonly employed on detection of an error in digital magnetic recording is a re-read cycle. A second or even third attempt will be made to read the data correctly before automatically signalling for attention. Another customary procedure in digital magnetic recording is to make an immediate readback check after writing. This procedure assures that the new data was correctly recorded, making this check while the original information is still readily available in the computer in the event a second attempt to write is required. Both these system procedures can be directly programmed and serve to counteract rare but inevitable bit failures.

A successful digital magnetic recording system is one that blends all the available design opportunities into an integrated whole to realize the performance objectives most effectively.

REFERENCES

1. *Information Transmission, Modulation, and Noise,* Mischa Schwartz, McGraw-Hill Book Company, Inc., New York, 1959.
2. "Universal High-Speed Digital Computers: Magnetic Store," F. C. Williams, et al., *Institution of Electrical Engineers Proceedings,* Vol. 99, Part 2, pp. 94–106, April 1952.
3. "Techniques for Increasing Storage Density of Magnetic Drum Systems," H. W. Fuller, P. A. Husman, and R. C. Kelner, *Proceedings of the Eastern Joint Computer Conference,* pp. 16–21, 1954.
4. "A Self-Clocking System for Information Transfer," L. D. Seader, *IBM Journal of Research and Development,* Vol. 1, No. 2, pp. 181–184, April 1957.
5. "Digital Computer Components and Circuits," R. K. Richards, D. Van Nostrand Company, Inc., Princeton, 1957.
6. "Pulse Time Displacement in High Density Magnetic Tape," R. A. Skov, *IBM Journal of Research and Development,* Vol. 2, No. 2, pp. 130–141, April 1958.
7. "Digital Magnetic Recording with High Density Using Double Transition Method," A. Gabor, *IRE National Convention Record,* 1960.
8. "High Density Digital Magnetic Recording Techniques," A. S. Hoagland and G. C. Bacon, *Proceedings of the IRE,* Vol. 49, pp. 258–268, January 1961.

INDEX